LAMENESS IN SHEEP

Agnes Winter

The Crowood Press

First published in 2004 by
The Crowood Press Ltd
Ramsbury, Marlborough
Wiltshire SN8 2HR

www.crowood.com

British Library Cataloguing-in-Publication Data
A catalogue record for this book is available from the British Library.

ISBN 1 86126 721 5

Acknowledgements
I am extremely grateful to a number of friends and colleagues who have helped me during the writing of this book. The Charnley family (Judith, Tom, Luke and Hannah), Michael Clarkson and Oli Hodgkinson have read the entire text and produced many helpful suggestions, which I have incorporated. In addition, I'd like to thank Dai Grove-White, Rob Smith, Richard Murray and Chris Lewis, with whom I have had discussions about specific aspects of lameness and its treatment. Veterinary student Caroline Marsh researched the detailed structure of horn for me. The editor of the *Veterinary Record* has kindly given me permission to use several of the photographs that I included in articles that I have written for the journal *In Practice*. Experiences over many years with my own sheep and those of clients and friends form the basis for the information in this book; and without the support of my late husband, Tom, I would not have been able to accumulate this degree of knowledge and experience.

Designed and edited by Focus Publishing, Sevenoaks, Kent

Printed and bound in Great Britain by CPI Bath

Contents

Introduction   4

1   Why Lame Sheep Matter   5
2   Equipment for Efficient Foot Care   9
3   Anatomy and Conformation   12
4   Trimming Feet   22
5   Footbathing Chemicals and Other Treatments   28
6   Overview of Diseases of the Feet   37
7   Scald   48
8   Footrot   52
9   Contagious Ovine Digital Dermatitis (CODD)   64
10   White Line Lesions   69
11   Pedal Joint Abscess   76
12   Granulomas   81
13   Other Foot Lesions   85
14   Lameness in Young Lambs   93
15   Other Causes of Lameness in Growing Lambs and Adults   105
16   Minimizing Lameness   114

Diagrammatic Summary for Diagnosis of Common
   Foot Lesions   119
Diagrammatic Summary for Eradication of Footrot   122
Glossary   124
Index   126

Introduction

Look at any field of sheep and there will almost always be some lame ones. So, why are lame sheep so common? Why does the problem not improve, in spite of the time and physical effort put into dealing with them? This book aims to show why lameness is so common, why the immense amount of time and effort put into treating lame sheep by many farmers often does not result in a significant reduction in the number of lame sheep, and how best to improve matters.

After considering why lame sheep matter, the book goes on to look at the equipment necessary to care for sheep's feet, and its correct use. It gives details of the anatomy of the foot, and shows how easily the foot can be damaged by unskilled trimming. Most importantly, it stresses the importance of making a correct diagnosis as to the cause(s) of lameness. To many people, lameness in sheep is synonymous with footrot. Whilst footrot is undoubtedly a very common cause of lameness, there are other common causes that might affect many animals in a flock – for example, scald and contagious ovine digital dermatitis – or that affect individuals or smaller numbers – for example, white line or pedal joint abscesses. Only when the sheep keeper has a clear understanding of the problems affecting his or her own flock can the most appropriate measures to treat and prevent the problem be implemented.

Separate chapters are devoted to the most important causes of foot lameness. Further chapters cover lameness in young lambs, and other forms of lameness in growing and adult sheep. The book concludes by bringing together in summary the important factors to consider in attempting to control and prevent lameness.

Having kept sheep for virtually the whole of my life, I am not naïve enough to think that all lameness in sheep can be prevented. All too often I find one or more of my own small flock lame (usually at the most inconvenient time). However, as a result of dealing with the problems that have arisen in my own sheep, I have come to recognize the range of causes, have eliminated footrot from my flock, and have experienced the fact that some sheep have very sound feet and are never lame throughout their whole lives whilst others have defective feet and are repeat offenders. During my professional life as a veterinary surgeon specializing in sheep I have seen and dealt with the whole spectrum of disease, from individual valuable rams crippled by lameness to whole flocks presenting a severe welfare problem.

I hope that this book will open people's eyes to the wide range of causes of lameness, and enable them to identify which are affecting their particular animals and thus to the best ways to treat and prevent the problems. I hope it will make life better for sheep by showing the damage that can be done by unskilled and unnecessary over-trimming of feet. I hope it will help sheep keepers to tackle the common infectious causes of lameness on a flock basis and thus reduce the number of avoidable cases of lameness. If it contributes to making life easier for both sheep and shepherd I shall feel that it has been worth the effort.

Agnes Winter, September 2004

1 Why Lame Sheep Matter

Lameness has been a major concern to sheep keepers for hundreds of years. William Youatt's book, *Sheep: their Breeds, Management and Diseases* written in the 1830s, refers to 'The dread and too frequent disease termed foot-rot' and says 'Prevention would … preserve the animal from disease and torture.' One hundred and seventy years later I shall be saying much the same thing in this book! The most obvious and important reason that we should be concerned about lame sheep is that they are in pain, and this should always be our primary reason for wanting to keep it to a minimum. However, there are good production and economic reasons why a significant degree of lameness within a flock should not be tolerated. Being lame reduces the amount of time a sheep

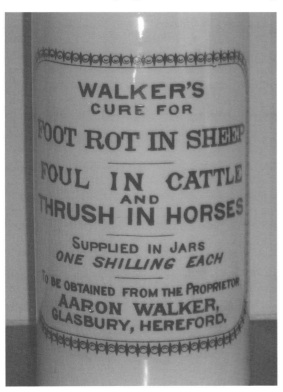

Footrot has beeen a concern for hundreds of years.

Lame sheeep are in pain.

The knees of this sheep show it had beeen lame for some time.

spends grazing, or makes it less able to compete for food where access or amount is limited. This means that affected animals will show reduced weight gain or even loss of weight, particularly if the lameness is very severe or prolonged in nature.

AN ACCEPTABLE PREVALENCE OF LAMENESS

'Prevalence' refers to the number of animals actually affected at a particular point in time, and the theoretical answer to the question 'What is an acceptable prevalence of lameness?' is 'nil'; however, this is a practical book which recognizes that there will always be a number of sheep that become lame for reasons beyond the control of the shepherd. The main aim should be to minimize the number of sheep lame for reasons that are preventable, namely footrot, contagious ovine digital dermatitis (CODD) and scald particularly. Flocks should certainly be aiming at a figure of no more than 2--3 per cent lame at any one time, with treatment of those as soon as is reasonably possible. A prevalence of above 5 per cent should lead to examination of the group or flock, diagnosis of the cause, and appropriate action. The Code of Recommendations for the Welfare of Sheep (2000) states that 'It [lameness] has clear adverse welfare implications', and although the code does not put a figure on the number of lame sheep that is 'acceptable', it can be assumed that the welfare status of a flock will be called into question if it contains many, particularly chronically, lame sheep.

EFFECTS OF LAMENESS ON PRODUCTION

Taking the yearly sheep production cycle, the most significant effects of having sheep lame at any particular point are as follows:

Tupping Time

Rams' feet should be kept in good condition throughout the year, but they should certainly be checked about two months before tupping time as a part of the pre-breeding check. Any problems found at this stage can then be dealt with so that the rams are in optimum physical condition when put out with the ewes. In the same way ewes' feet should be checked and treated where necessary, as a part of preparation for the breeding season. The overall result of ewes and rams being lame at tupping time is likely to be an increased proportion of barren ewes and reduced number of lambs born at lambing time because

● lame rams are unlikely to be able to mate with as many ewes as sound ones;
● lame rams are likely to have a reduced sperm count, and are therefore likely to be less fertile than sound rams;
● lame ewes are less likely to be at an optimum condition score at mating, therefore may have a lower ovulation rate, and therefore produce fewer lambs;
● lame ewes spend more time lying down, therefore may not actively seek out the ram when in season;
● lame ewes may not be able to stand the weight of a heavy ram mounting during mating, and therefore stand more chance of being barren.

First Month of Pregnancy

At this early stage of pregnancy, ewes should be stressed as little as possible because the developing embryos are not firmly implanted in the uterus. Having lame sheep, or gathering sheep for treatment, are both avoidable forms of stress. Any increased stress at this stage, or greatly reduced feed intake, can lead to increased embryo death, therefore contributing to a reduced number of lambs born.

Last Third of Pregnancy

This is the stage at which the ewe must maintain as much condition as possible in order to produce healthy lambs and be able to rear them successfully. The effects of ewes becoming lame at this time are:

● increased risk of metabolic diseases, especially pregnancy toxaemia (twin lamb disease) because of insufficient food intake;
● increased ewe and lamb mortality rates as a result of metabolic disease;
● reduced lamb birthweights, therefore decreased survival rate, and increased labour inputs required to try to maximize survival;
● reduced colostrum production, therefore decreased lamb survival rate because of hypothermia and infections such as joint ill;
● reduced milk production, therefore reduced lamb growth rates.

Note that these are all effects of being lame in late pregnancy, although the results may not be seen until after lambing.

Lame rams will have reduced fertility.

Lame ewes are likely to produce less milk for their lambs.

At Lambing Time

The effects of ewes being lame at this time may seriously affect surviving lamb numbers, in that the ewes will also suffer from:
● decreased colostrum and milk production;
● increased clumsiness, leading to a higher risk of injury or even death in the lambs;
● increased bacterial contamination of the lambing area (particularly if the ewes are affected by footrot), leading to increased risk of navel and joint ill in lambs.

During Lactation

Again, lameness among the ewes might have a serious knock-on effect, causing
● decreased milk production, and a premature drying off;
● difficulty for lambs gaining access to teats to suck;
● lambs feeding from behind the ewe get dirty heads, which may predispose to fly strike.

Growing Lambs

Lambs have a reduced growth rate, and therefore take a longer time to achieve the requisite slaughter weight; furthermore in the case of replacements, these may fail to achieve the target weight for mating if being they are being bred as ewe lambs.

ECONOMICS OF LAMENESS

The reduction in production that may occur in a flock with a significant number of lame sheep will depend on whether the lameness is of short duration or whether it is a chronic, continuing problem. Taking the example of a 100-ewe prolific flock normally producing 1.75 lambs per ewe, a reduction of only 0.1 lambs per ewe reared will mean ten fewer lambs sold, and therefore a likely loss of at least £400 (based on finished lamb prices at the time of writing), since costs of production will remain similar.

If there is a chronic flock problem throughout the whole annual production cycle, the added cost of extra gathering and handling, together with cost of treatment, should also be taken into account. The actual costs of all these are often not recognized. Estimates of £6.50 loss per lame ewe have been made.

If an individual ram becomes lame he may be unable to work and is likely to need replacing. This is bad enough if it is a commercial ram costing a few hundred pounds, but it is a financial and breeding disaster if a very expensive pedigree ram is involved; therefore the economic facts alone mean that a lameness problem should be treated seriously. But in the end, remember lameness means pain and poor welfare.

2 Equipment for Efficient Foot Care —

Many shepherds put much energy and time into the examination and treatment of the feet of their sheep, particularly the obviously lame ones, yet the overall level of lameness in many flocks often does not fall. This is usually because the infectious forms of lameness are not tackled on a whole-flock basis, often simply because of the amount of effort involved in examining (not necessarily trimming) every foot of every sheep. If a flock affected by footrot is to be tackled seriously with the intention of reducing lameness to a very low level, then a lot of hard work will inevitably be involved in the process of achieving this goal. But the end result is definitely worthwhile because, once under control, few individual animals will require treatment, and for the main flock, footbathing alone may be all that is required in the long run. Foot care and lameness control can be made much easier by having the best possible equipment available. The essentials are:

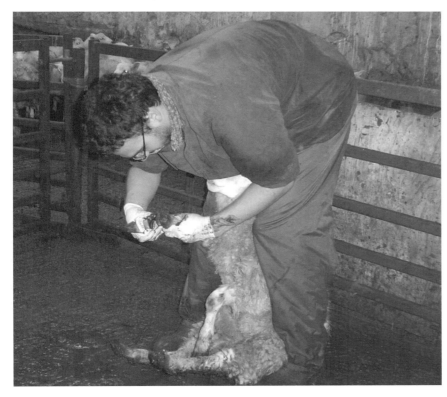

Trimming feeet is hard physical work.

9

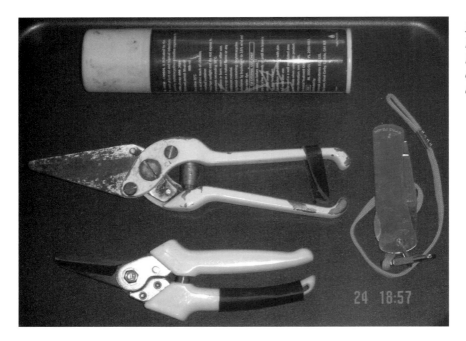

Foot clippers and knives should b e kept in good condition and not allowed to go rusty.

● Well maintained, sharp foot shears and knives. These should be cleaned, disinfected and oiled at the end of each session so that they do not become rusty and inefficient to use. For information on the technique of trimming feet, see Chapter 4.

● A good handling system on hard standing that can be cleaned easily. There should be a dry area on which sheep can stand after treatment: all the hard work of turning sheep, examining feet and treating will be wasted if sheep are immediately turned back to wet grass. The sides of the pens should be free of sharp projections, and the floor should not consist of sharp stones as both can cause injury to feet and legs. A suitable handling system can be anything from a simple hinged gate hung across the corner of a pen for a small hobby flock, to a home-made set of pens, or a commercial pen arrangement. Portable commercial systems may be used if sheep are grazing away from the main farm buildings, but these will usually be used on grass and will soon become dirty underfoot unless

the weather is very dry. In this situation there is unlikely to be a suitable hard area for sheep to stand after treatment.

● For other than the smallest flocks, a turnover crate so that feet can be examined without the shepherd having to bend over. For small numbers, a

Well maintained, home-made pens.

A portable handling system.

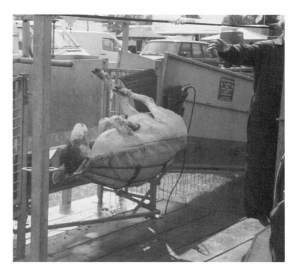

Try out turn-over crates before purchase.

shepherd's chair, which looks a bit like a deckchair, is worth considering, although it can need two people to sit a heavy sheep in this. A variety of crates is on offer commercially, but be careful to try them out before purchase – the effort required to turn sheep varies considerably between the different types. A system that allows sheep to be turned with a minimum of effort and does not require constant bending is more likely to lead to thorough examination of the whole flock if this is necessary.

● A footbath or baths of a size suited to the size of flock and choice of chemical to be used. If a 'stand-in' product such as zinc sulphate is to be used, the bath must be sufficiently large to accommodate a reasonable number of sheep at one time. It is worth considering having two baths, with plain water in the first to wash mud off the feet before the sheep go into the second treatment bath. For very small hobby flocks a bucket or plastic feed bowl may be an adequate substitute. For further information about the use of footbaths, see Chapter 5.

A footbath is essential for all but the smallest flock.

11

3 Anatomy and Conformation

THE ANATOMY OF THE FOOT

The wild ancestors of domesticated sheep originally evolved in dry, mountainous or almost desert environments. Here, the growth and the wear of horn kept pace with each other, resulting in the self-maintenance of hard, well shaped feet. In the UK, the hooves of mountain sheep kept extensively tend to follow the same pattern and usually require little attention. But as soon as sheep are kept at higher stocking densities on lush grass in the lowlands, and particularly when they are housed, problems with the feet are likely to begin because of the damper conditions leading to softening of the horn and the rapid spread of infectious foot diseases in such environments. In addition, the tendency has been to select for production traits such as higher lambing percentages and faster growth rate, with little attention being paid to foot soundness.

Although the basic anatomy of the foot is the same for all sheep, in practice the shape of the feet varies considerably from one ewe to another. Most shepherds will be familiar with the fact that some sheep have neat, well shaped feet throughout their life, whilst others constantly overgrow or have repeated episodes of lameness. There appears to be quite a lot of variation in foot soundness between and within breeds in both foot shape and horn

![Healthy feet needing no trimming.]

Healthy feet needing no trimming.

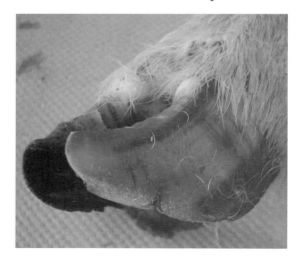

Foot with an overgrowth of the wall of both claws.

12

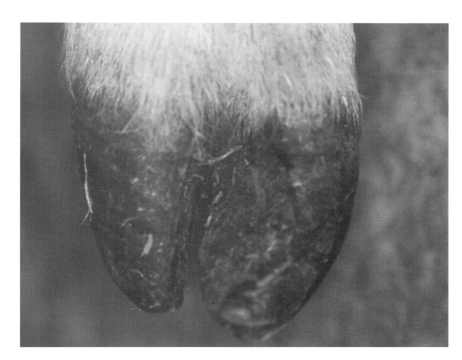

A normal-shaped claw to the left, a corkscrew claw to the right.

Foot with very poor quality soles.

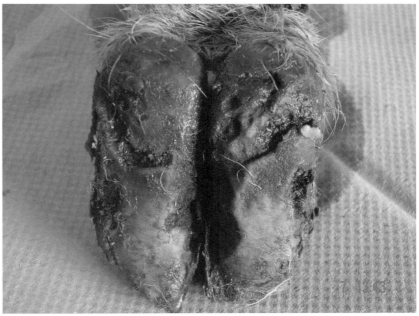

strength, although the environment in which the sheep are kept will also have an influence. Personal experience with my own animals has shown me that foot shape and health in animals kept in the same environment, be it indoors or outdoors, varies greatly and is an area that could be tackled in genetic improvement programmes (see Chapter 16).

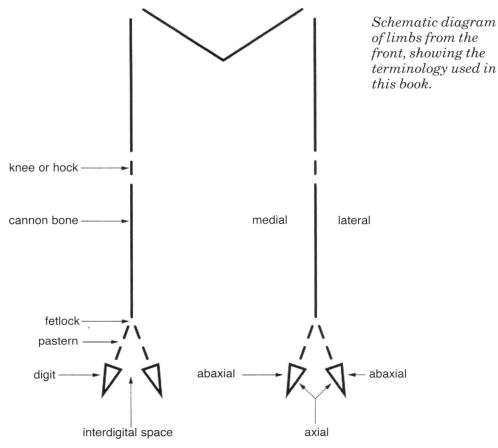

Schematic diagram of limbs from the front, showing the terminology used in this book.

knee or hock

cannon bone

medial lateral

fetlock

pastern

digit

abaxial abaxial

interdigital space

axial

The foot of the sheep has two digits (claws, hooves) and two accessory digits ('dewclaws'): the outer claw is known as the lateral claw, and the inner claw as the medial claw. The outer side of each claw is called the abaxial wall and the inner side is the axial wall. The horn covering the claws is highly modified skin and is the equivalent of the human fingernail. Separating the claws is the interdigital space that consists of normal skin covered by short hairs.

The coronary band is the dividing line between the hoof and the normal skin above the hoof. In the skin above the hooves in the midline is the opening of the interdigital gland. This structure consists of a deep, narrow tube of skin with many sebaceous (wax-producing) glands. The secretions probably act as

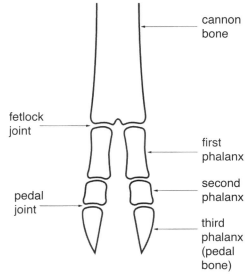

cannon bone

fetlock joint

first phalanx

second phalanx

pedal joint

third phalanx (pedal bone)

Diagram of the bones of the lower part of the leg from the front.

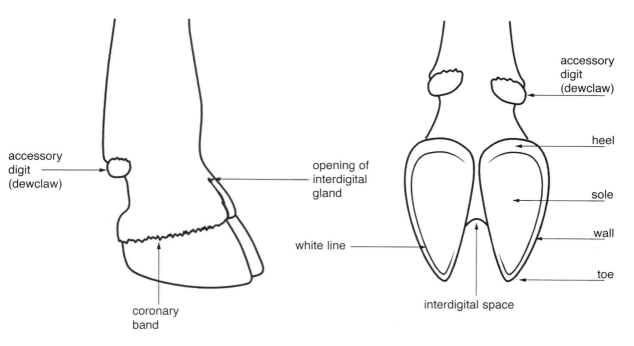

The foot from the side.

The foot from below.

scent-markers in wild sheep, allowing flocks to keep track of the movement of individuals. Occasionally the duct gets blocked and the gland enlarges and becomes obvious as an egg-shaped swelling protruding at the top of the interdigital space.

THE STRUCTURE OF THE HOOF

The hoof consists of essentially three layers: the horn capsule, the corium and the pedal bone.

The Horn Capsule

This horny capsule protects the deeper structures of the foot. It consists of the hard horn of the wall, the soft horn connecting the hard horn to the skin of the coronary band called the periople, the soft

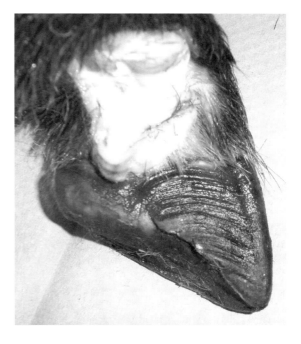

Slaughterhouse specimen with one claw removed to show the axial wall.

15

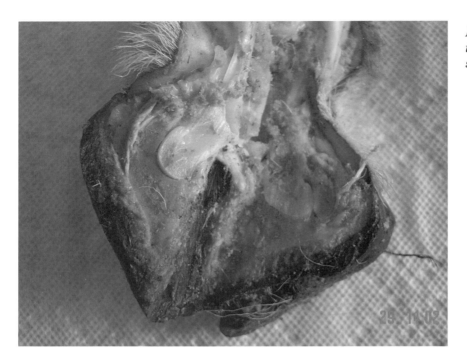

Hoof sawn in half to show the inside structures.

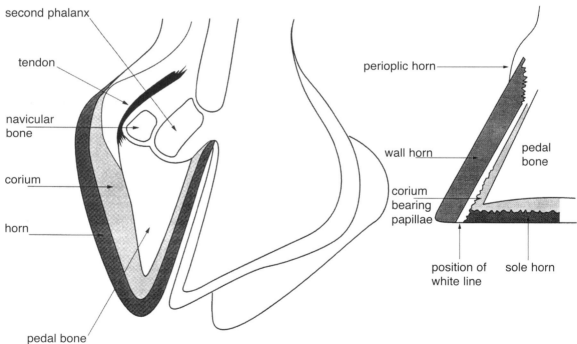

second phalanx

tendon

navicular bone

corium

horn

pedal bone

perioplic horn

wall horn

pedal bone

corium bearing papillae

position of white line

sole horn

Diagram of structures visible in the section of the foot shown in the preceding picture.

Section through the hoof showing the relationship of the wall horn, the sole horn and the white line.

16

horn of the heel, and the horn of the sole which is not as hard as the wall but harder than the heel horn. The junction of wall and sole horn is called the 'white line' (see page 20). The horn may be white or pigmented, or a mixture of both. Pigmented (black) horn is thought by some to be stronger than unpigmented (white) horn. The inside of the hoof wall carries a series of laminae, like the pages of a book, which connect the wall firmly to the underlying corium (the 'quick'), but also allow flexibility as the animal walks. When the horn is damaged, infection can get under the horn into the deeper layers of the foot, producing an abscess. In footrot and CODD, the infection separates the horn from the underlying corium, the sensitive part of the foot.

The Corium

Otherwise known as the 'quick', the corium lies between the horn capsule and the pedal bone. This is the part that contains blood vessels and nerves, and on its surface has papillae (small projections covered in dividing cells) that are

Foot trimmed to show white line.

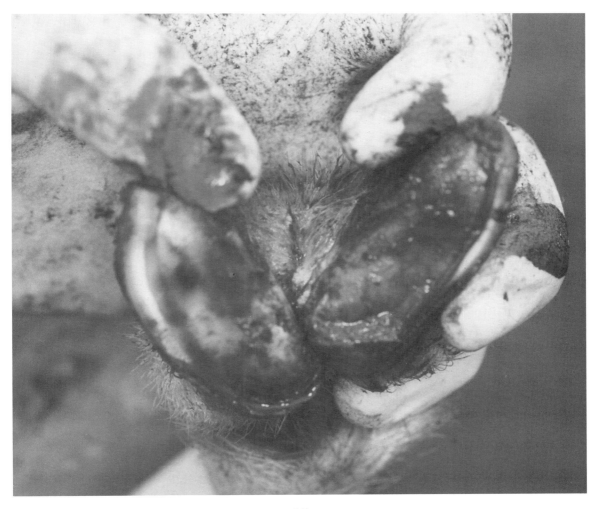

Diagrammatic representation of horn formation.

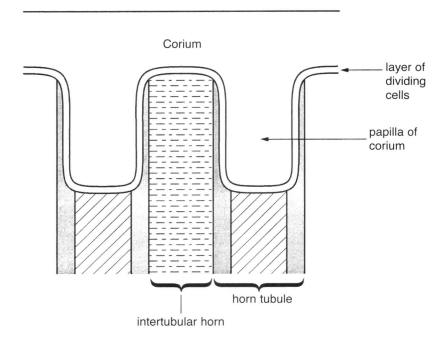

Corium

layer of dividing cells

papilla of corium

horn tubule

intertubular horn

responsible for producing the hoof horn. When the corium is cut or damaged, the foot bleeds and the animal feels pain. If infection gets in through a crack in the horn an abscess may form in the corium, and pus may spread underneath the wall. This is very painful, like having infection under a fingernail, though once the abscess bursts the animal usually recovers. The 'quick' is also exposed in footrot and CODD, both of which are very painful diseases.

The Pedal Bone

Otherwise called the third phalanx, the pedal bone is the main bone of the hoof and lies almost entirely within it. Infection of the pedal bone, and other deep structures within the hoof, is extremely painful and has serious consequences for the sheep. These other structures are:
● the small navicular bone, which lies behind the pedal bone (this causes a lot of problems in horses, but not in sheep);
● the pedal joint that separates the pedal

bone from the pastern bone (the second phalanx). This joint contains a lubricating fluid, joint fluid, which allows the ends of the bones, which are covered in cartilage, to move easily on each other;
● tendons that attach to the front and back of the bones of the foot, and which allow the animal to straighten or bend the foot (these are the equivalents of the tendons that allow you to move your fingers);
● around some of the tendons are structures (tendon sheaths) containing lubricating fluid, which assists movement of the joints and tendons;
● ligaments bind the bones together and prevent the claws splaying apart.

FORMATION OF THE HOOF HORN

The horn is formed by rapidly multiplying cells covering and separating microscopic papillae that project from the surface of the corium. As these cells mature they fill with a hard protein called keratin (this forms hair as well as horn), and move away from the corium to form the denser part of the outer hoof wall. In the hoof wall, these cells form as a series of longitudinal microscopic tubules, each tubule produced by a single papilla. The tubules are held together by softer intertubular horn produced from the cells separating and surrounding the papillae. As the wall horn grows, it gradually moves downwards over the laminae at the rate of about 1mm a week (though this is a very approximate figure, since there is much variation in the growth rate of hoof horn in sheep). Excess horn is worn off at the base of the wall as the animal walks. The feet of animals with access to hard ground will generally wear at a faster rate than those on soft ground, but there is much variation between individual sheep as to whether rate of wear equals rate of growth.

Horizontal grooves indicate a period of illness in this animal.

19

Check the hind-leg conformation,
particularly in rams.

The horn of the sole is also produced from papillae, on the corium of the sole, and consists of a series of short horn tubules bound together with intertubular horn. Unlike the wall, the sole has no laminae.

At the junction of the horn of the wall and that of the sole is the area called the white line, so-called because, when the hoof is cleaned up, it can be seen as a line of unpigmented horn. The horn of the white line is not as strong as wall horn and can therefore be a weak point in the hoof. White line disease is quite common, and infection can get in, leading to abscess formation under the wall (see Chapter 10). In horses' feet, the white line is the part of the hoof into which the nails attaching the shoe are driven.

Because the production of horn is a continuous process requiring a constant supply of nutrients, any reduction in available feed, or loss of appetite caused by illness, will affect the amount and strength of horn produced. This shows up as horizontal grooves in the hoof wall; shallow grooves reflect the varying quality of the diet, and deep grooves reflect more serious food deprivation or serious systemic illness.

CONFORMATION OF THE LIMBS

As well as considering foot soundness, it is worth looking at overall leg conformation and health, particularly in rams and in pedigree or purebred breeding ewes. Leg conformation varies quite widely, both between and within breeds. Poor or weak leg conformation can lead to reduced length of useful breeding life, and in extreme cases, to actual lameness. The most common conformational faults are as follows:

● Very upright hind legs with over-extension of the hock joint – these are what I would describe as being like 'turkey legs', where the hock is completely straight rather than being angled as in a normal leg. The extra strain put on the hock joint can lead to arthritis and thickening of the bone round the hocks.

● Long, sloping pasterns, where the fetlocks sink almost to the ground; this sometimes leads to the development of arthritis.

● Deviation of the lower parts of the hind legs towards the midline – these animals walk in a rather 'bow-legged' fashion, and the foot of one leg may catch and brush against the inside of the other leg at each stride. Whilst this may not cause lameness in itself, the animal often has deformities of the claws (for example a narrow outer claw, and a wide, bent inner claw) because of the abnormal stresses placed on the feet by the abnormal stance.

● Knock knees – this also does not directly cause lameness, but may lead to abnormal claw growth in the front feet.

Essentially when selecting breeding stock, particularly rams, look for a leg at each corner, sound conformation of the hocks, upright, springy pasterns and healthy, well shaped feet with claws of approximately even size.

4 Trimming Feet

Foot trimming is often seen as a routine task that must be done once or more every year in order to keep sheep's feet sound. In fact, many sheep have their hooves trimmed unnecessarily, and their feet may even be damaged by unskilled over-paring. In the normal sheep's foot, the wall is usually slightly higher than the sole of the hoof – this is a natural feature enabling the majority of the weight of the animal to be taken on the strong outer hoof wall. Even if the wall is pared back to the level of the sole it will soon re-grow, so no useful purpose is performed in paring this type of foot. Trimming by itself has no part to play in preventing infectious forms of lameness such as footrot, and is only useful for the following purposes:

● to improve foot shape when the horn is significantly overgrown or loose;
● to remove trapped mud, stones or other debris;
● to help in making a diagnosis of the cause of lameness;
● to remove obviously loose horn before footbathing or applying another form of treatment.

When trimming an overgrown but basically sound foot, horn should never be cut so deeply that it bleeds – this is both painful for the sheep (think what it feels like if you tear your nail so deeply that it bleeds!) and is very likely to cause a granuloma (strawberry-like growth – see Chapter 12), which will cause the sheep to be chronically lame.

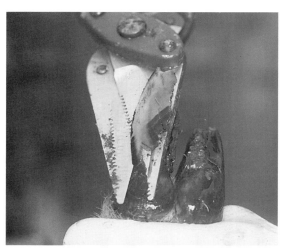

Keep the blades parallel to the sole when trimming excess wall.

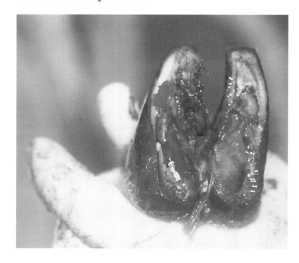

The feet should not be trimmed so hard that they bleed.

If the flock is infected with footrot or CODD, gathering sheep for 'routine' foot trimming (or any other procedure) and then releasing them without footbathing, or footbathing incorrectly, can also lead to problems. Both these infections spread in the close contact of dirty handling pens, therefore it is not surprising that the lameness situation in such a flock can become worse in succeeding weeks.

Examining the feet can be a dirty and smelly job – wearing disposable gloves is a sensible way of protecting the hands. These can be discarded after examining very infected feet, and a new pair used to protect uninfected feet against cross-contamination. At the end of a session where foot trimming has been carried out, hoof parings should be swept up and disposed of by burning, as they can act as a source of infection to other animals passing through the pens.

It is useful to distinguish between trimming basically sound, but overgrown feet; examining the feet of a lame sheep; and carrying out a whole flock examination in an attempt to eradicate footrot, since the technique may be slightly different, depending on the particular objective.

PRELIMINARY EXAMINATION OF THE FOOT

Often the sole is covered by a hard layer of mud or, in the case of housed sheep, a 'shoe' of dried manure. This should first be cleaned away so that the shape of the foot can be clearly seen. This can be done using a sharp knife or the points of the foot shears, taking care not to actually stick them into the foot proper. If there is no significant overgrowth of the walls and the foot looks sound, leave it at that. A small amount of overgrowth of the walls is not worth trimming, providing the underlying foot is sound, as the wall will quickly re-grow.

Infected Feet with Maggot Infestation

During the fly season it is common to find diseased feet infested with maggots. Although maggots are now used for cleaning up wounds in people and undoubtedly do clean up infected feet, this is no excuse for leaving the feet untreated. Foot strike often leads to body strike, which can rapidly become life-threatening if not quickly noticed and dealt with.

Infected feet often become infested with maggots during hot weather.

TECHNIQUE FOR TRIMMING AN OVERGROWN FOOT

Unlike the routine for trimming cows' feet, there are no accepted guidelines on measuring the foot to assess how much excess horn can be cut off; this is largely because there is so much variation in the shape of individual feet. If the foot is significantly overgrown, keeping the foot clippers parallel to the sole, carefully cut away obviously loose or excess horn in order to bring the foot to as normal a shape as possible, but do not cut so deeply that any blood is drawn. Remember that there is no need to make the wall completely level with the sole. Take particular care at the toe where it is very easy to take too deep a bite of horn. Be careful on the axial (inner) side of the claw at the point where the wall horn meets the softer horn of the heel: there is a natural shallow crack here where sometimes a loose flap of horn can be found. It is easy to cause damage and bleeding by trying to remove this flap too close to the base, so it is best just to cut off

Overgrown foot before trimming.

The same foot after trimming.

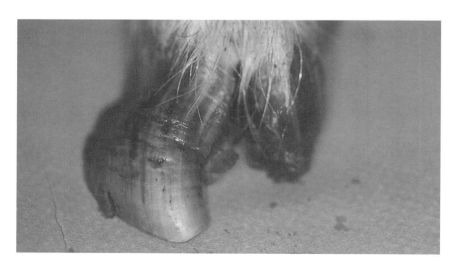

A claw with a grossly distorted wall...

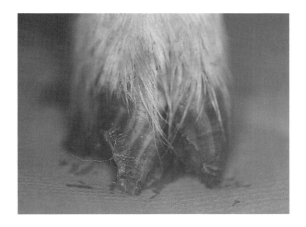

...and the same foot adequately trimmed without causing bleeding.

The claw on the right has a rotated wall - do not attempt to trim any further.

the obvious flap itself and not attempt to go any deeper.

Feet with White Line Separation

This problem is dealt with in detail in Chapter 10. However, it is common to find sheep with a small degree of white line

separation, which are not lame at all. In these cases, it is worth paring away the loose piece of the wall to remove the underlying pocket in which mud is trapped so as to prevent a more serious problem developing. The detached horn only should be cut away with a sharp knife; this usually leaves a characteristic

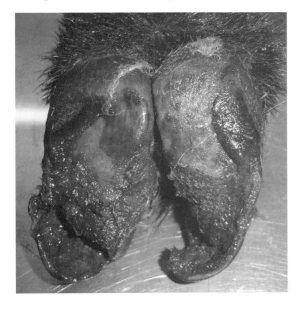

Loose flaps of horn at toes – be careful not to cut too deep.

The axial walls have cracked, producing loose flaps of horn.

A footrot case lightly trimmed before footbathing.

half-moon appearance with keratinized laminae visible. You should not cause any bleeding during this procedure.

Misshapen Feet

Many sheep have basically sound but abnormally shaped feet, most commonly abnormally long narrow claws or corkscrew-shaped claws. Particular care must be taken when trimming these, and it may not be possible to achieve a normally shaped foot. Corkscrew claws are especially difficult to deal with, as the hoof wall is rotated and becomes the weight-bearing part in place of the sole, which itself is very narrow. The abnormal wall often continues to grow, since the edge of it is not subject to the usual wear; this then becomes wrapped over the sole. Trimming should only involve the excess wall, stopping where the wall meets the sole, and no attempt should be made to cut more deeply into the abnormally curved wall.

Misshapen feet also result from chronic disease such as recurrent white line infections, chronic footrot, or chronic infection of deeper structures within the foot. In these cases, the affected claw may be enlarged with production of excessive soft, poor quality horn. Again, it will usually not be possible to return the foot to a normal shape, and care must be taken not to cut too deeply causing bleeding. Such animals are often best culled, as they will be a constant source of problems.

PARING THE FOOT OF A LAME SHEEP

The cause of the lameness may be obvious, or a more thorough examination may be necessary to determine the cause. The routine for this is described in more detail in Chapter 6. If the foot is affected with white line degeneration, the loose piece of wall can be pared away (see Chapter 10). If the foot is affected with footrot, only obviously detached horn should be removed, in order that footbath chemicals can penetrate. Even this trimming may not be necessary, as it has been shown that daily footbathing in zinc sulphate with no trimming can be successful in treating footrot.

Animals affected with severe footrot are best treated with an antibiotic injection and left for a few days before any foot trimming is done. (See Chapter 8 for more details of treatment for footrot.)

WHOLE FLOCK EXAMINATION

This will be necessary in a flock with a significant number of footrot or CODD cases, in order to separate out and treat infected sheep. Full details of treatments are given in Chapters 8 and 9. Techniques for the reduction or even eradication of footrot are well known. Not enough is known about CODD at the time of writing to be sure that the same techniques will work for eliminating this disease, but it is safe to assume that identification and separation of infected animals will be an important part of disease control.

A foot should only be trimmed sufficiently to identify whether it is infected or not, and to remove obviously loose horn. There is no need to trim hard back, and the feet should not be trimmed so hard that they bleed. The secret of successful treatment lies in the segregation of infected animals, correct use of footbathing, and/or injectable antibiotic to bring about a cure, if possible, and the regular footbathing and monitoring of the remainder of the flock to ensure that early cases have not been missed.

If the eradication of footrot is to be attempted, the feet should be examined more carefully in order to identify possible carrier animals that may have less visible disease in cracks and crevices in the feet; however, paring should yet again not be so severe as to cause bleeding. Adequate and repeated footbathing in zinc sulphate will usually deal with minor lesions, but animals with grossly abnormal feet that cannot easily be pared to an acceptable shape are better culled.

5 Footbathing Chemicals and Other Treatments

For most flocks, the use of one or more footbaths is an essential part of a foot-care programme. Their use will certainly be necessary in the treatment and control of the infectious forms of lameness – scald, footrot and CODD -- in all but the smallest flock.

> NOTE: the information given in this chapter regarding the use of chemicals or antibiotics applies to flocks kept for breeding purposes. Care should be taken to check whether a meat withdrawal period applies (this will definitely be the case with antibiotics) if animals are close to slaughter. For milking flocks, you may find there are restrictions on the use of certain products for lactating ewes. Always read the product instructions and check with your veterinary surgeon or the manufacturer if in doubt.

Some drugs cannot be given to lactating ewes.

TYPES OF FOOTBATH

There is a wide range of footbath designs, ranging from commercially produced metal, rubber or plastic, to home-made concrete. In addition there are various types of absorbent mat that can be used in baths or independently. If the sheep's feet are very dirty, it is worth having two footbaths if possible, the first filled with plain water to wash their feet, before they enter the second bath containing the chemical. This is particularly important if formalin is being used, as this is denatured (deactivated) by organic matter such as soil and faeces.

Obviously, concrete baths form part of a permanent handling system, and other

Footbath constructed for use with a large flock.

A permanent stand-in footbath constructed from concrete.

There is usually a good selection of footbaths and other equipment at agricultural events.

large baths are not very portable. Smaller baths may be sufficiently portable to move to the site where they are required. The footbath(s) is only one part of a successful handling system and should be situated alongside suitable pens and on, or adjacent to, hard standing where sheep can be held for a minimum of 30min after treatment.

It cannot be stressed too much that, particularly when dealing with footrot or CODD, if sheep are put through a footbath, but then turned out immediately on to damp or long grass, the footbathing chemical will almost immediately be washed off the feet, and all the hard work in handling the sheep will go to waste. Only in the driest of summer weather is it

This large farm has hard standing adjacent to the handling pens.

worth considering tackling a flock problem by footbathing, and then immediately letting the sheep back on to grass.

An exception is where scald in growing lambs is the main problem and they are grazing away from the main farmstead, when it may be necessary to footbath in a situation where there is no hard standing. As scald is only a superficial infection of the interdigital skin, treating in less than ideal conditions may be sufficient to maintain control to an acceptable level. One possible approach is to place a footbath in a narrow gateway between fields so that the sheep are forced to walk through it as they move between fields; however, this will not be practicable in wet weather as the approaches will become muddy and the contents of the bath will be diluted by rain. If this method is used, the footbath should contain zinc sulphate, as formalin will quickly degrade in this situation.

Alternatives for Small Flocks

For the treatment of individual feet, a bucket, bowl or other container may be all that is necessary. If zinc sulphate is being

This large gathering area could become muddy in wet weather.

used, however, it can be rather tedious to have to restrain the sheep for the required length of time. Furthermore, remember that if only obviously lame sheep are treated by this method and an infectious type of lameness is present, other sheep in the flock are likely to be infected, and control on a flock basis will never be gained.

Absorbent mats can be useful for providing prolonged treatment, particularly if the affected sheep are housed. If the mat is placed in front of a feed trough or rack, the sheep will be forced to stand on the mat in order to eat. This system is most useful if zinc sulphate is the product of choice, as repeated use has no adverse effects on the hoof horn, whereas repeated use of formalin can cause the horn to become hard and brittle.

FOOTBATHING CHEMICALS

Formalin

This chemical has been used for many years for the control and treatment of both scald and footrot. Formalin is usually supplied as a 40 per cent solution of formaldehyde in water. To make the required strength it should be diluted as follows:

For 5% formalin solution, add 1 part 40% formalin to 19 parts water
For 3% formalin solution, add 1 part 40% formalin to 32 parts water
For 2% formalin solution, add 1 part 40% formalin to 49 parts water

Advantages
● Cheap
● Effective for both scald and footrot
● Sheep need only walk through slowly
● Acceptable in organic farming systems

Disadvantages
● Unpleasant, with irritant vapour

A totally inadequate footbath in a handling system adjacent to the gathering area in the previous photo.

● Toxic if inhaled, ingested or absorbed through skin
● Probable carcinogen
● Becomes denatured by organic material (mud, faeces, straw etc.)
● Painful on damaged tissue
● Can damage hooves if used at too strong a concentration or too frequently
● Can splash into sheep's faces and damage the eyes, particularly if animals are hurried through the bath

In spite of this long list of disadvantages, formalin is still commonly used because it is cheap and effective. However, it should be handled carefully and not used in a confined space. It is possible that regulations on its use may be tightened in the future, so care needs to be taken to keep up with any changing advice. Formalin should not be used for treating severe cases of footrot as it is extremely painful.

Uncontaminated formalin solution is quite stable, but will eventually break down to formic acid and ultimately to carbon dioxide and water. Solutions that have been contaminated with soil and faeces, such as occurs in normal flock footbathing procedures, will break down much faster and are likely to need replacement after one day's use. The common practice of putting straw in the bath to aid movement of sheep through also leads to faster breakdown of the formalin because straw is an organic material.

Zinc Sulphate

This is usually supplied as a white crystalline powder of zinc heptahydrate, but occasionally may be as zinc monohydrate. It may also be supplied as a solution. The directions on the container should be followed for mixing, but in general it is usually used as follows:

Zinc sulphate is the preferred treatment for footrot.

For 10% solution using the heptahydrate, add 1kg to 10ltr water

For 10% solution using the monohydrate, add 650g to 10ltr water

Some commercial products contain a surfactant (detergent) that speeds up penetration of the zinc into the hoof. A few squirts of washing-up liquid added to products that do not already contain a surfactant will do the same job.

Advantages
● Very effective against footrot, effective against scald
● Non-painful on damaged tissue
●Stable in solution even when contaminated

Disadvantages
● Relatively expensive
● Sheep need to stand in the bath (how long depends on the product and on the severity of the disease, but a minimum of 2min, up to 30min)
● Toxic if drunk
● Can be slow to dissolve

Zinc sulphate is a popular and effective choice for treating footrot providing the handling system allows for the necessary stand-in time. It may not be the first choice for treating scald where even a stand-in time of 2min may be impractical if speed of treatment is an important factor. Zinc sulphate solutions can be used repeatedly, though care needs to be taken that it is neither concentrated by evaporation in hot weather, nor diluted by rain in wet weather. Very contaminated solutions can be cleaned up by sieving before re-use. Although there is a recent report of it being ineffective against one strain of footrot in Australia, there is no evidence currently of similar problems in the UK.

Copper Sulphate

This is available as blue crystals ('blue stone') that dissolve easily in water to form a blue solution. Although it is an effective treatment for footrot, it is no longer commonly used because copper is very toxic if ingested by sheep. If used at all, it is made up as a 5 per cent solution (1kg to 20ltr water).

Copper sulphate crystals may be useful in small amounts as one method of treating toe granulomas (see Chapter 12).

Antibiotics

No antibiotics are licensed for use in footbaths for treating sheep in the UK. However, they are being used for dealing with severe cases of lameness due to CODD, which are often unresponsive to more orthodox treatments. Those that have been successfully used are lincomycin/spectinomycin or tylosin soluble powder. Dilution rate is 100g to 200ltr water for both. These products must only be used on the advice of a veterinary surgeon, who can supply them or issue a prescription, and will give you information such as withdrawal time if applicable. Use of antibiotics in footbaths should be strictly limited to circumstances where no other treatment has been found to be effective. Antibiotic footbaths are known to be effective against footrot, but should not be used because other recognized non-antibiotic products are available, and from the point of view of guarding against possible antibiotic resistance problems developing in the future, it is preferable to use other chemicals where possible.

Other Products

A number of other chemicals have been/are promoted for use in footbaths for sheep; these include benzalkonium chloride and various mixtures of organic acids. These usually act, at least in part, as disinfectants and are often described as 'for maintaining foot health' or 'effective at killing bacteria on feet'. If you intend to use them for treating infections such as scald, footrot or CODD, you should check with the instructions that they have been shown to be effective.

Disposal of Footbath Liquids

There are strict controls on the disposal of chemicals into the environment, but often little thought is given to the method of disposal of spent footbath contents. If in doubt, the advice of the Environment Agency should be sought, as an authorization under the Groundwater Regulations 1998 is likely to be required for disposal on to land. Alternatively contact a licensed waste disposal contractor. Any escape of footbath contents into watercourses is likely to have serious consequences.

● Formalin is probably the easiest to dispose of safely as it breaks down to water and carbon dioxide. It is probably best left to stand for a few days, then diluted well before putting into a slurry tank.

● Zinc sulphate can be repeatedly re-used so the question of disposal will arise less frequently, but when due for disposal it should be dealt with under the above authorization or by a waste contractor.

● Copper sulphate is toxic to sheep and should never be disposed of on to land where sheep might graze.

● Antibiotic footbaths are often disposed of into slurry stores, but this practice is very dubious as it exposes vast numbers of bacteria to the particular antibiotic used, and the possibility of antibiotic resistance developing as a result may arise at some time in the future. It would be useful to have clear guidelines on disposal and perhaps some recognized methods of denaturing the chemical before disposal,

as is possible with some sheep dips. I can only repeat that you should seek advice if you are not sure.

SPRAYS

Antibiotics

The most commonly used product in this category is oxytetracycline, supplied by your veterinary surgeon under several different brand names as an aerosol spray, usually containing a blue dye (it used to contain gentian violet but no longer does so because of safety concerns). This is an effective way of treating scald or early cases of footrot, but animals should be

Antibiotic foot sprays are effective for scald and early footrot cases.

kept on dry ground for 30min after treatment to allow time for the product to work. Turning treated animals immediately back on to wet grass is usually a waste of time and money. This type of spray should be used as an alternative to, and not in addition to, foot bathing. Antibiotic sprays are not adequate to treat severe cases of footrot, since insufficient penetration of the foot will occur.

Other Products

Other aerosols are available containing chemicals such as cetrimide. This is a general antiseptic; if used, a check should be made to see that it is having a beneficial effect.

INJECTABLE ANTIBIOTICS

The only way that these are legally obtainable in the UK is either directly from your veterinary surgeon or on a prescription supplied by your veterinary surgeon. The use of injectable antibiotics should be considered for treating the following disease situations:
- severe footrot cases;
- cases of CODD;
- individual lame sheep with foot abscesses.

The following antibiotics are most commonly used for lameness: long-acting oxytetracycline; penicillin/streptomycin combination; tilmycosin.

Long-Acting Oxytetracycline

The usual dose rate is 1ml/10kg by deep intramuscular injection (sometimes splitting the dose and injecting at two sites may be recommended), but check the data sheet, as some products require a larger dose for prolonged effect. This is

very effective against footrot, and may be useful for foot abscesses. It is worth test-dosing a few cases if CODD is suspected, as it may not be effective for this condition and therefore might be a waste of money if used immediately on a flock basis. The injection may be painful and may cause temporary discoloration at the injection site.

Penicillin/Streptomycin Combination

This has been shown to be effective against footrot, but the dose required is double that recommended (the usual recommended dose is 1ml/25kg, so increase to 2ml/25kg, but remember to check with the particular product being used). It may be helpful for cases of foot abscess, but is not usually effective for CODD. This is also injected into the muscle but is less painful than oxytetracycline.

Tilmycosin

This product is effective against both footrot and CODD. It is relatively expensive and requires care in handling. It is not recommended for treating animals under 15kg bodyweight as there is a risk of overdosage; for larger animals a reasonably accurate estimate of bodyweight is necessary. It has the advantages of low volume (1ml/30kg), and administration by subcutaneous (under the skin) injection.

Withdrawal Periods

Remember always to check the length of this. Withdrawal periods for some antibiotics have been extended and may be many weeks, which limits their use in animals close to slaughter. The use of most antibiotics is prohibited in sheep producing milk for human consumption.

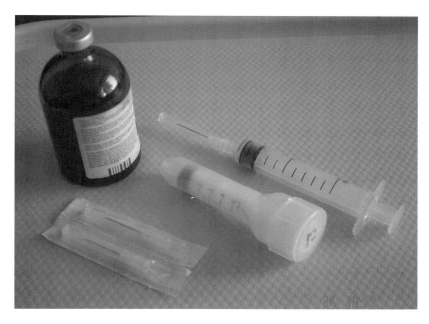

Sterile syringes and needles should be used for giving injections.

NOTE: Extreme care needs to be taken by the person administering the injection since it may have toxic effects on humans if accidentally injected. IF THIS HAPPENS, IMMEDIATE MEDICAL HELP SHOULD BE SOUGHT, taking the package insert with you.

Injection Technique and Site

It is important that injections of any type should always be given in a clean manner using sterile, disposable needles. Areas of wet or dirty fleece should be avoided, as the injection site is likely to become contaminated, leading to abscess formation. Subcutaneous injections are best given under the skin of the neck by lifting a 'tent' of skin and injecting into the fold. Intramuscular injections are also best given into the neck area of sheep, as this part of the carcass is of low value compared with the muscles of the hindquarters. If the hindleg has to be used because of lack of muscle in the neck, the safest area is the quadriceps muscle that lies in the thigh in front of the femur, the main leg bone. Injections should not be given into the back of the thigh, as important nerves run through this region and may be damaged, leading to temporary or even permanent partial paralysis of the leg (see page 110).

Young lambs should preferably be injected under the skin if the product can be given by this route. If injection into a muscle is required, the safest place is into the muscle in front of the thigh. Sterile dog-size vaccination syringes and needles (a 2ml syringe with a 21g ⅝in needle, obtainable from your vet) are suitable for this.

VACCINATION

There is currently only one vaccine of relevance to the control of lameness in sheep, specifically for controlling footrot. It consists of ten strains of *Dichelobacter nodosus*, the organism that causes footrot, in an oil adjuvant (this helps to stimulate the immune response produced by the body in response to the injection). This vaccine is of no use whatsoever for controlling lameness other than footrot. It

Beware Injectable Moxidectin

Sheep that have been vaccinated with footrot vaccines at any time in the past should never be given injectable moxidectin (a worm treatment) since fatal allergic reactions have been reported. There does not appear to be any difficulty with the reverse – i.e. vaccinating sheep that have previously had injectable moxidectin does not cause problems.

injection site. These can, on occasion, be large and may burst, discharging pus
● May cause pigmentation in the overlying wool
● Can cause serious medical problems if injected into humans – immediate medical help should be sought if this happens
● Relatively costly (but take into account the reduced handling of infected animals that will be needed)
● May need at least two doses per year, depending on weather and individual flock circumstances.

OTHER MEASURES

is particularly important, therefore, that diagnosis of the cause of lameness is correct before use of this vaccine is considered (see Chapter 6).

Advantages
● Will help to treat, as well as control, footrot
● Very useful in heavily infected flock to reduce prevalence at start of intensive control programme

Disadvantages
● Often produces a reaction at the

Use of Lime

Applying builders' lime to gateways or areas where sheep congregate is sometimes advocated. Lime is alkaline, therefore changes the pH (acidity or alkalinity) of the soil and may help to reduce the bacterial load, particularly where scald is a problem.

6 Overview of Diseases of the Feet

Correct diagnosis of the cause of lameness is essential.

It is often assumed that lame sheep and footrot are synonymous. Whilst it is true that footrot is a very important cause of lameness, there are many other causes. Correct diagnosis is important whether one sheep or a hundred are affected, since it is a waste of time and money applying an inappropriate treatment. This chapter will help you to decide on the correct diagnosis before moving on to specific treatments described in later chapters. If a number of sheep are lame, the most likely cause is an infection – scald, footrot or CODD. Do not rely on the examination of only one or two animals to decide on diagnosis because some may not show the typical appearance – for example, a healing case of footrot where disease is left in only one part of the foot; a case of simple scald where other cases may have progressed to early footrot; a severely infected foot that could be either virulent footrot or CODD. Always look at a number

of feet to get a clear picture and to establish whether more than one type of lameness is present in the flock.

In growing and adult sheep, the foot is the most likely seat of lameness, so it is logical to examine this first. If no abnormality can be found, then the remainder of the leg can be examined (see Chapter 15). In young lambs it is most likely that joints will be involved (see Chapter 14). For a diagrammatic summary of diagnosis of common foot problems, see pages 119–121.

EXAMINATION OF THE FOOT

If the foot is clean and is showing classic signs of scald or footrot, diagnosis may be straightforward. In many cases, however, a thorough examination of the foot may need to be done in order to establish what the exact problem is. The following steps, together with reference to the diagrams of the typical appearance of the various forms of lameness, should enable an accurate diagnosis to be made. The directions on foot examination may appear to be unnecessarily complicated and detailed for someone who is already experienced at examining sheep's feet, but are intended as a guide for the less experienced, or in cases where the cause of lameness is not obvious. It is also useful to know for how long the animal or animals have been lame. An animal that goes lame overnight (acute onset) may have scald or a foot abscess. Footrot takes longer to make the animal really lame. Bony thickening in the area of the coronary band takes several weeks to develop and indicates a chronic problem. Remember that if you have a flock problem, several animals should be examined to be sure that you have the whole picture. Observe the following procedure:

1. If the foot is dirty, clean off any mud or manure. This can usually be done using a knife or the points of hoof shears, but take care not to damage the foot. If the foot is really dirty it may be necessary to clean it with water (soaking if necessary) and a soft brush.

2. Separate the claws and examine the cleft for evidence of scald. If the cleft is impacted with dried mud or manure, this should be removed. It is also quite common to find small sticks or stones trapped in the cleft. Any of these will cause damage to the interdigital skin, with soreness developing and invasion with the bacteria that cause scald. There may be other interdigital lesions such as interdigital hyperplasia (fibroma) or discharging sinuses signalling deeper problems in the foot.

3. Examine and compare the appearance of the hooves. There may be obvious swelling or enlargement of one claw when compared with the other. This may indicate infection deeper in the foot, for example a pedal joint abscess. The horn capsule may be partially or completely detached in CODD or virulent footrot. In the case of toe granulomas, these may be so large that they are immediately obvious, or they may be smaller and covered by loose horn.

4. Check if there are any abnormalities above the coronary band. A chronic pedal joint abscess will show hair loss with discharging sinuses in the skin above the affected claw. Hair loss is also often seen with CODD.

5. Look at the wall of each hoof for cracks or grooves. If grooves are present, examine the other feet to see if they are present on only one or on all feet. Shallow grooves often do not cause problems, but deep grooves lead to weakening of the horn of the wall and infection may get in, leading to abscess formation.

A deep horizontal groove or crack on one claw suggests the problem is localized to that hoof only and is usually a sign that there is/has been an abscess under the

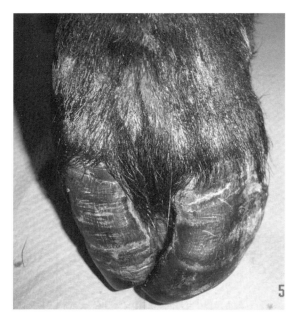

Deep groves can crack, allowing infection to get under the horn.

wall. A vertical crack may also indicate an abscess that has damaged the horn-producing tissues at the coronary band. Shallow horizontal grooves usually indicate variations in nutritional status. Deep horizontal grooves on all claws suggest that the animal has suffered from some systemic illness such as pregnancy toxaemia, sickness after a difficult lambing, mastitis or laminitis.

6. If there is no obvious horn detachment, examine each hoof carefully. Pain, such as that caused by an abscess, can be localized to one claw by applying gentle pressure by squeezing each claw in turn. Feel each claw for signs of heat that could indicate an abscess.

7. Look at the sole of the hoof and scrape or pare lightly if necessary. Some sheep have poor quality sole horn that looks flaky and white, but underneath, the sole may be sound. Occasionally a foreign body such as a sharp stone or wire may be sticking into the sole. Classic footrot is indicated by underrunning and detachment of part of the sole, starting near the heel towards the back of the cleft.

8. If there is no sign of footrot or other obvious problem, pare carefully along the white line area, looking for evidence of white line disease. This may be indicated by one or more discrete black marks or more extensive separation of the wall from the underlying laminae.

If no abnormality can be found in the foot after having examined it thoroughly, continue by examining the rest of the leg (see Chapter 15).

DIAGNOSTIC FEATURES OF COMMON FOOT CONDITIONS

Soil Balling/Impaction in the Cleft

Soil balling is usually obvious as soon as the foot is examined, although a small

Soil balling is easy to diagnose but difficult to prevent.

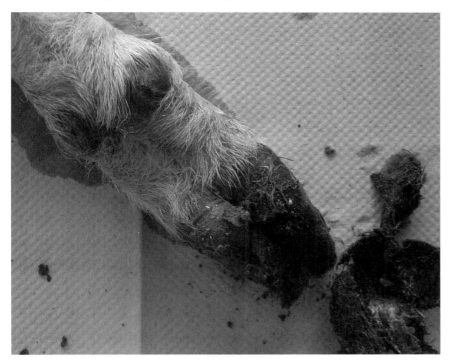

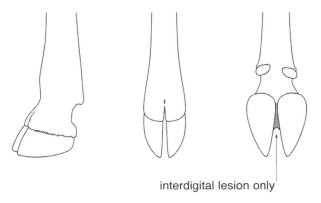

interdigital lesion only

Scald.

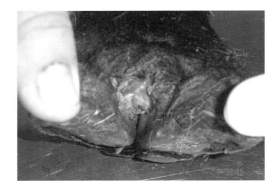

Early scald lesion.

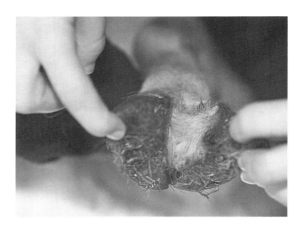

Typical scald case.

stick or stone may be hidden deeply between the claws and is therefore less obvious. Lameness may be the direct result of whatever is impacted in the cleft, or may be made worse by superimposed infection with scald.

Scald (Interdigital Dermatitis)

This is an infection limited to the skin between the claws. The skin, which is either inflamed or whitish in colour, is damp and slightly swollen. Often the short

hairs on the interdigital skin are lost, particularly where the bulbs of the heels rub together. If scald is present, a careful check should be made to see whether this is progressing to early footrot, with separation of the sole just beginning. In simple scald, there is no separation of the horn.

Interdigital Hyperplasia (Fibroma)

Here, an outgrowth of skin occurs from the skin/horn junction in the cleft of the foot.

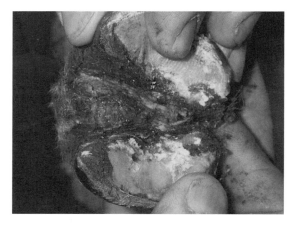

Interdigital hyperplasia with concurrent scald infection.

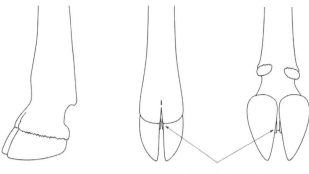

Interdigital hyperplasia.

one or two skin folds may be present

Often two outgrowths are present, one growing from each side. In young animals, these are often insignificant but enlarge with age and may become chronically infected. In addition, the sides of these growths often become secondarily infected with scald.

Footrot

Classic footrot follows infection with scald, and begins with separation of the sole from the underlying deeper tissues. This

Early case of footrot showing a typical site of separation of the horn.

in virulent footrot, underrunning continues across sole and up wall

underrunning starts from interdigital space near heel and spreads across sole

Footrot.

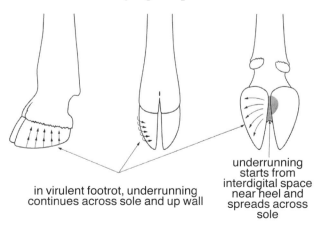

Virulent footrot affecting both claws.

41

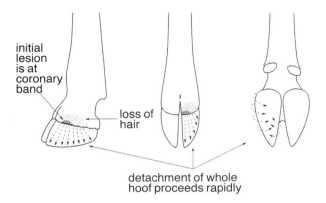

initial
lesion
is at
coronary
band

loss of
hair

detachment of whole
hoof proceeds rapidly

Contagious ovine digital dermatitis (CODD).

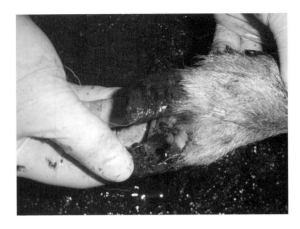

Early CODD lesion at the coronary band.

CODD lesion showing the loss of hair above the coronary band.

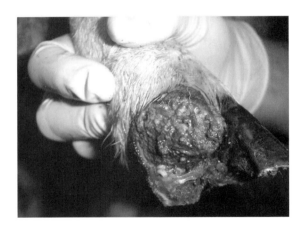

CODD lesion showing loss of hoof horn.

starts towards the heel on the axial side of the claw and, depending on the type of footrot, may spread across the sole and partially or even completely up the wall of the hoof. Even in virulent cases, the horn often remains attached at the toe. The underrunning is usually accompanied by a characteristic smelly greyish discharge.

Contagious Ovine Digital Dermatitis (CODD)

This disease seems to have a different course from footrot in that it starts with a

Sometimes it is difficult to decide whether an animal is suffering from virulent footrot or CODD.

lesion at the coronary band, then progresses swiftly down the hoof, undermining the whole horn capsule, which may become completely detached. There may be no interdigital involvement, but hair is often lost from the skin above the foot.

In some cases it may be difficult to distinguish a very severe case of footrot from CODD.

White Line Degeneration (Shelly Hoof)

In this extremely common condition, part of the hoof wall becomes detached from the underlying laminae along the course of the white line. The extent varies from minor separation of little significance, to extensive separation with mud and debris becoming impacted in the pocket under the wall. When the loose horn is pared away, a characteristic half moon appearance often remains. This should not be confused with footrot. In advanced cases, pus may form under the wall, at which stage the animal becomes acutely lame. The pus usually eventually bursts at the coronary band.

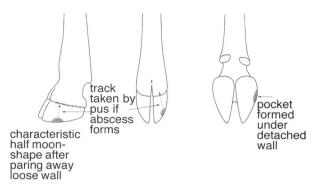

White line degeneration (shelly hoof).

White Line Abscess (Toe Abscess)

Here, the fault in the white line is much more discrete and is marked by one or more black marks along the course of the white line, anywhere between the toe right along to where the soft horn of the heel begins. The animal is acutely lame and the affected claw is hot and painful. If untreated, pus makes its way up the line of least resistance to the coronary band, where it bursts out. It may also undermine a small part of the sole locally, but this is

Typical appearance of shelly hoof.

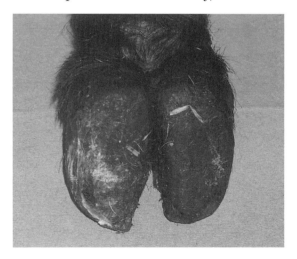

Foot showing black marks in white line.

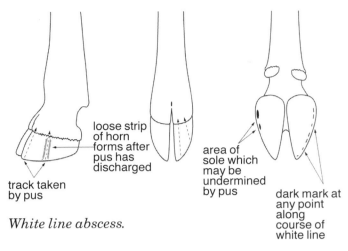

White line abscess.

Slaughterhouse specimen with a white line abscess (do not pare the foot of a live animal like this!).

Under-run area of sole resulting from an abscess in the white line – do not confuse with footrot.

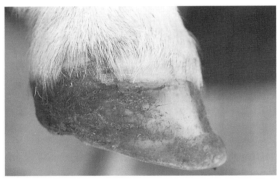

Horizontal crack in the hoof wall following a white line abscess.

always on the outer (abaxial) side of the sole, and should not be confused with footrot. If the horn is carefully pared in the region of the black marks, pus may be released (very satisfying!), but more commonly, a good flow of pus is not found. Some sheep have repeated attacks of lameness due to this condition, presumably because of defective horn formation at this site.

Horizontal and Vertical Cracks

A horizontal crack in a single hoof usually indicates a previous white line abscess, and shows where pus burst out at the coronary

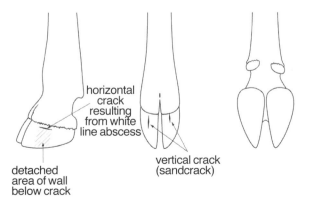

Horizontal and vertical cracks.

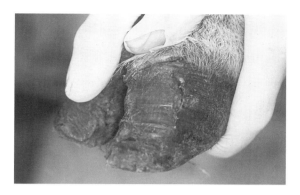

Vertical sandcrack.

Pedal Joint Abscess

This is a serious condition where infection gets into the joint deep within the hoof.

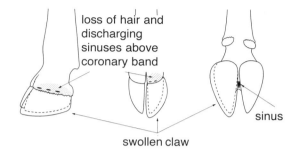

loss of hair and discharging sinuses above coronary band

swollen claw

sinus

Pedal joint abscess.

band. As the horn grows, the crack moves downwards and eventually grows out. The animal may become lame again as the defect gets near to the bottom of the hoof wall and develops into a larger crack, a bit similar to a crack in a finger nail that extends into the sensitive part causing pain.

Vertical cracks (sand cracks) usually indicate previous injury to horn-producing tissue at the coronary band. These may grow out or be permanent, depending on the extent of the damage. Infection may get in through the crack, leading to pus formation and lameness.

The animal is acutely lame, usually being unable to take any weight on the foot. The affected claw becomes swollen, and pus bursts out at several points around the coronary band. Often the first place it bursts is in the cleft of the hoof, and the discharging sinus may be marked by red granulation tissue that bleeds when touched. Hair is usually lost from the area above the hoof around the discharging sinuses. If untreated, the condition

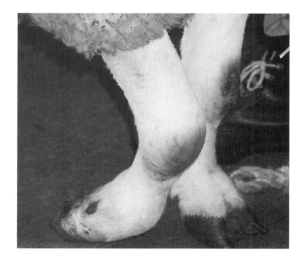

Severely lame ram with pedal joint abscess.

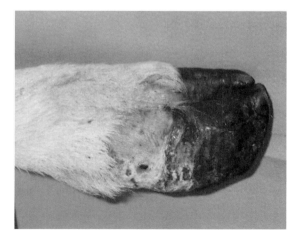

Pedal joint abscess showing hair loss and evidence of discharging sinuses above the coronary band.

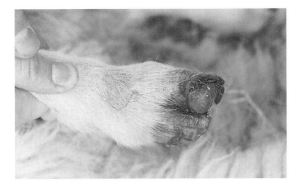

Typical appearance of a granuloma.

becomes chronic and the animal remains very lame. The hoof often becomes enlarged and deformed. In some cases a slow recovery of sorts occurs, allowing the animal to bear some weight, but the claw never returns to normal.

Granuloma

These are found most commonly at the toe, and take the appearance of a strawberry-shaped piece of proud flesh, often covered loosely by overgrown horn. When trimmed they bleed profusely. Occasionally they may occur in the sole,

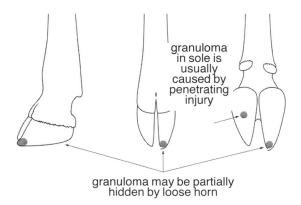

granuloma in sole is usually caused by penetrating injury

granuloma may be partially hidden by loose horn

Granuloma.

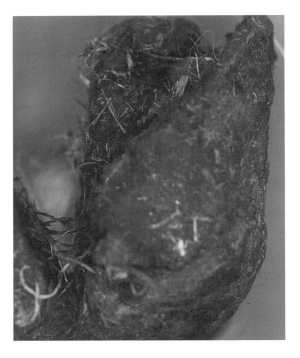

A granuloma partially hidden by loose horn.

usually as the result of injury, or along the wall in conjunction with footrot.

Laminitis

This is not particularly common in sheep, but when it occurs the animal is acutely lame on all four feet. Initially there may be little to see, apart from the feet feeling hot. As the condition progresses, deep horizontal lines or grooves appear in the horn of all the hooves just below the coronary band; this is because of interference with normal horn growth. Grooves may be single or multiple, depending on the duration of the illness, and they gradually move down the hooves as the horn grows. Cracking may occur in the weakened horn.

Other Causes of Lameness

As the foot is the commonest site of lameness in adult and growing sheep, this

46

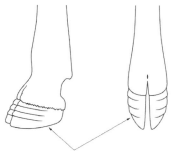

grooves on all claws of all feet
(may crack)

Laminitis.

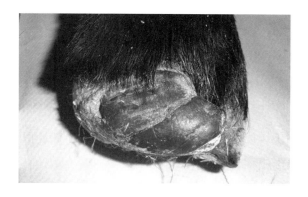

Severe laminitis.

is the obvious place to start your examination. If no foot abnormality is found, the remainder of the limb should be examined. Conditions affecting other parts of the limbs, and exotic diseases causing lameness such as Foot and Mouth disease, are described in Chapters 13, 14 and 15.

HAVING MADE A DIAGNOSIS...

The descriptions, diagrams and photographs in this chapter should have given you a sound base on which to make a diagnosis if the foot is the site of the problem, whether one sheep or one hundred are involved. Information regarding the treatment and prevention of the important types of lameness is given in the following chapters.

A diagrammatic summary of diagnosis of common foot problems appears on pages 119–122.

7 Scald

Scald – otherwise known as interdigital dermatitis, scad, strip or benign footrot – is caused by a bacterium called *Fusobacterium necrophorum*, which is widely distributed in the environment, particularly in mud and also in faeces. It can live in the environment for long periods and cannot be eradicated, therefore every sheep flock is potentially at risk of this condition, although it is claimed that in some flocks in which footrot has been eradicated, scald is not seen either. However, personal experience with my own flock is that scald does still occur, usually in growing lambs, in spite of the fact that footrot has been eradicated. It is also possible that benign (non-invasive) strains of *Dichelobacter nodosus*, the causal organism of footrot, may cause scald. For more information on this organism, see Chapter 8.

DIAGNOSTIC FEATURES

Scald is most common in growing lambs, but can also affect older animals. Affected animals often become acutely lame, so can go from being normal to very lame overnight. Usually at least several animals, and often a larger number, are affected at the same time.

Infection with scald is limited to the skin of the interdigital space. The bacteria are not able to damage and undermine horny tissue, therefore cannot, on their own, cause footrot (see Chapter 8). The skin of the interdigital space is damp, slightly swollen and usually reddened, but can sometimes be whitish. The short hairs covering the interdigital skin may be lost, particularly towards the back of the space where the heel bulbs rub together. The degree of

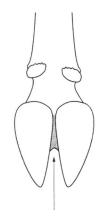

Scald.

interdigital lesion only

48

Typical appearance of scald.

Examine the cleft carefully to see whether the lesion is scald or early footrot.

lameness often seems out of all proportion to the abnormalities that can be seen, so it is obviously a very painful condition. More than one foot may be affected.

TREATMENT

The condition is painful and should therefore be treated, although, providing that no footrot is present in the flock, animals affected with scald will eventually get better, particularly if conditions underfoot dry up or they are moved to drier grazing with short grass. Another important reason for treating this condition is that, as few flocks are entirely free of footrot, an untreated scald outbreak could rapidly escalate into a full-scale footrot problem if it takes place in weather conditions conducive to the spread of footrot.

Treating Small Numbers

Spray the interdigital space with oxytetracycline aerosol. If possible, the treated animals should be kept on dry standing for half an hour to give the treatment time to work, but if only a few animals are affected and the flock cannot be brought in, it is still worth catching and treating individual affected animals out at grass. The efficacy of this treatment has been questioned by some people, but my experience is that it is very effective.

Treating Larger Numbers

The group will have to be gathered and treated on a flock basis, since it is impossible to pick out all lame animals when they are bunched together; also, treating the whole group is the first step in controlling the problem. It is possible to treat large numbers with an aerosol spray, but it is expensive, and both labour- and time-consuming; the cheapest and most practical treatment is to walk the whole group slowly through a footbath of 2--3 per cent formalin, then hold them on dry ground for half an hour before turning back to grass, ideally to a pasture that has not carried sheep for five to seven days. Usually a single treatment will result in a cure (though not prolonged control). The contents of the footbath will quickly become contaminated with mud and faeces, so a fresh solution will need to be prepared before each treatment session.

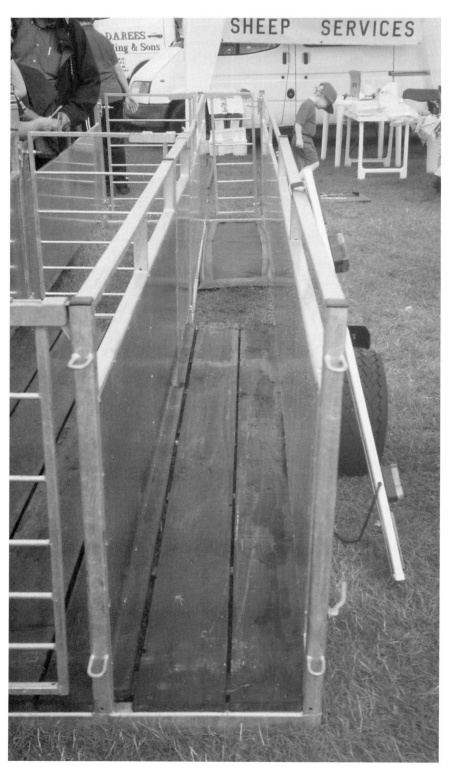

A narrow race will take a walk-through bath or mat suitable for treating scald.

As an alternative, 10 per cent zinc sulphate solution can be used. This is kinder on the feet than formalin, but takes longer. A slow walk through a long footbath should be effective, but a quick hop, skip and jump through a short footbath is unlikely to provide sufficient contact with the chemical.

If housed animals are affected, treatment may be complicated because hard lumps of bedding are attached to the feet. In the case of small numbers of sheep, these lumps can be removed by hand, but if a larger number is involved it will help if the animals are allowed to stand in plain water to soften the bedding material or walked across hard core before being walked through the medicated bath.

CONTROL

Scald is particularly difficult to control other than by regular footbathing because of the ubiquitous nature of the causal bacteria. It is also because prolonged wetting of the skin of the interdigital space in wet weather or when animals are on lush grazing allows infection to enter easily. Housing sheep on poorly maintained, damp bedding also predisposes to infection. Control can therefore be assisted in the following ways:

● Keep grazing short (sheep do best on a grass length of 4–6cm anyway).
● Try to avoid having muddy areas where animals congregate, such as around feed troughs and in gateways. I know this may be almost impossible in wet weather, but frequent moving of troughs or racks and good maintenance of gateways with appropriate use of hard core will help.

● Make sure that for housed animals, pens are free-draining and the bedding liberal and well maintained. Feeding silage of a very low dry matter can cause pens to be unacceptably wet. If hay is fed, excessive wastage as bedding can be a problem, as bedding with a high hay content is more likely to form hard lumps of manure on feet, than is straw.
● Put sheep through a footbath of 2–3 per cent formalin (no stronger otherwise feet are likely to become excessively hardened) on a regular, perhaps weekly, basis during the main risk period, which is when grass is growing rapidly in late spring and again in the autumn. It is best if animals can stand on dry ground after treatment, but if they are grazing away from the farm and a portable handling system has to be used, I would still recommend treatment on welfare grounds, if possible on a dry day, even though the conditions may not be ideal.

Although attempts have been made to develop a vaccine to control scald, these have not so far been successful. This seems to be because there is little immunity produced to the causal organism, although the fact that adult sheep are less commonly affected than lambs suggests the possibility of there being some resistance developing with age, but there may be other explanations. Another interesting observation from my own (limited) experience is that Black Welsh Mountain sheep and their offspring have hardly been affected with scald, when white sheep of other breeds grazing with the black ones have been affected; so perhaps there is breed or individual variation in susceptibility that could be exploited.

8 Footrot ─────────────────

Footrot is caused by a bacterium called *Dichelobacter (Bacteroides) nodosus* acting in conjunction with *Fusobacterium necrophorum*, which is the cause of scald. Both these bacteria thrive in the absence of air and are described as 'anaerobic'. The initial damage done to the interdigital skin in the scald infection allows the footrot bacteria to invade the skin. These produce enzymes and toxins that attack horn and enable the bacteria to progressively undermine and damage the horn of the hoof, leading to the under-running and foul smell characteristic of footrot. Other bacteria invade and contribute to the damage and inflammation in the foot, but *D. nodosus* is the crucial organism involved. Unlike *F. necrophorum*, which is widespread in the environment, *D. nodosus* lives in sheep's feet and can only survive in the environment for a maximum of about two weeks. It is very important to realize that footrot is an infectious condition that relies on the presence of infected feet to maintain the infection within a flock. Unlike scald that cannot be eradicated from a flock because it is widespread and long-lived within the environment, footrot can be eliminated and a flock can be maintained footrot-free, providing the infection is not reintroduced.

There are ten different groups of *D. nodosus*, called serogroups. These vary in virulence – that is, in the amount of damage done to the foot of the sheep by the enzymes (proteases) that the bacteria produce. Some strains of the bacteria are associated with benign footrot, that is when the disease is mild with little or no under-running of horn. In these cases, healing may occur spontaneously, especially in dry weather, and response to footbathing or even antibiotic spray treatment is good. Other strains are associated with virulent footrot, where the under-running of the horn and associated inflammation is much more extensive. Although some of these cases will eventually self-cure, some animals will remain persistently infected and will act as a continuous source of infection to other animals. The severity of the disease can also be influenced by the degree of natural resistance of individual sheep, and by the environment in which the infected animal is being kept.

Although self-cure may eventually take place with cases of footrot, failure to treat infected animals on this basis is not acceptable, since recovery is often prolonged, with accompanying pain and suffering throughout this period. Also, during the time of blowfly activity, which may extend from late spring through to autumn, sheep with footrot often become infested with maggots, and these can spread from the feet to the fleece leading to blowfly strike, which can be fatal if untreated.

TRANSMISSION PERIODS

Much work on footrot has been done in Australia, where transmission and nontransmission periods for the disease are recognized. Essentially, the bacteria spread easily between sheep in warm (above 50°F, 11°C), damp conditions but not in hot, dry (Australian summer) or cold conditions. In the UK, transmission periods are less well defined because of the damper climate and warmer winters. However, it can be assumed that the disease is unlikely to spread in hot, dry summer weather or in very cold winter weather. It should be noted, though, that housing sheep does allow the disease to spread, particularly if the bedding is poorly maintained and damp. This means that if in-lamb ewes are housed several weeks before lambing and some are infected with footrot, the disease is likely to spread substantially during the housing period as the incubation period is only ten to fourteen days. There are two important conclusions as a result:

1. The best time to tackle footrot on a flock basis is in hot, dry weather. In the UK, this means summer, particularly after weaning when lambs have been separated from the ewes. This does NOT mean that footrot should be ignored at other times of the year though.

2. Ewes' feet must be healthy at housing. It is definitely worth making the effort to separate infected ewes into a single group so that treatment of those can be instigated and others do not become infected. Footbathing the healthy group before housing will also help to ensure that problems during the housing period are minimized.

DIAGNOSTIC FEATURES

Apart from benign footrot, which may progress no further than a scald-type lesion, footrot is distinguished by invasion and separation of the hoof from the underlying structures. One or more claws on one or more feet may be affected. The separation starts at the heel near the back of the interdigital space and may not be easy to spot initially. Applying pressure with the fingers to the heel of the foot will show more easily if there is any early separation. In virulent footrot, this separation soon extends across the sole

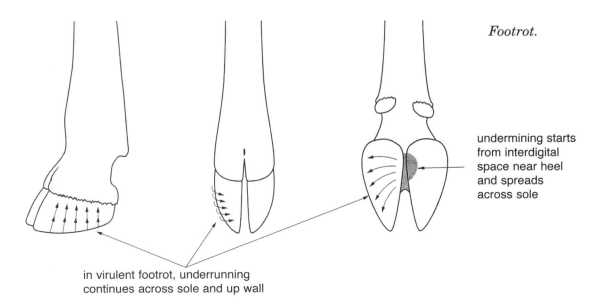

Footrot.

undermining starts from interdigital space near heel and spreads across sole

in virulent footrot, underrunning continues across sole and up wall

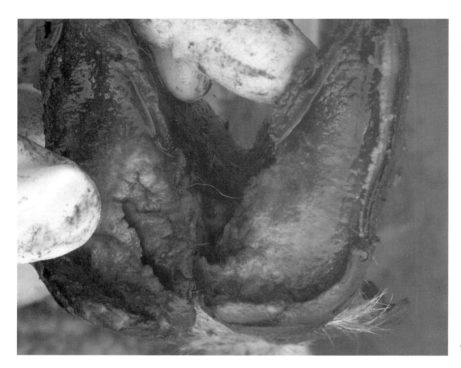

Early footrot showing separation at the heel.

Footrot with separation proceeding across the sole.

Virulent footrot affecting the soles and the walls of the claws.

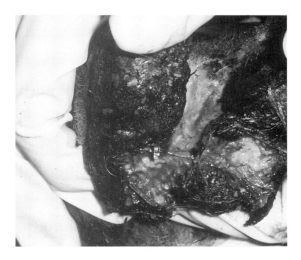

A severely infected foot that responded well to antibiotic injection.

Stand-in footbath for treating with zinc sulphate.

and up the lateral wall, and dead tissue produced by the action of the bacterial toxins gives rise to the characteristic grey, smelly debris under the loosened horn. Eventually, most of the horn capsule may be undermined and detached – by which stage the affected animal will be extremely lame. Ultimately, most sheep will recover even if untreated, but recovery may be prolonged, and the affected feet may be left misshapen with pockets of infection remaining, and these will act as a source of infection for other animals. Immunity to a natural infection is weak, so animals may become repeatedly infected.

During warm weather blowflies are often attracted to infected feet so that infestation with maggots is quite common. If present, these should be removed even though it could be argued that they would assist in cleaning up the feet. Maggots can spread from the feet to the body (commonly behind the shoulders), leading to severe cases of fly strike.

Classification of Types of Footrot

A scoring system developed in Australia by Professor John Egerton is a useful method for recording the severity of disease in individual feet; it also allows an assessment to be made of the overall extent of the disease in a particular flock. The scoring system is as follows:

If most of the affected sheep have lesion scores of no more than two, the outbreak is described as 'benign' and should

Score	Description
0	Normal hairy skin in interdigital space
1	Loss of hair and mild inflammation of interdigital space
2	Necrosis of interdigital skin with ridging and erosion of interdigital skin, but no separation or under-running of horn
3	Under-running of soft horn of posterior part of sole and heel, starting at posterior part of interdigital space
4	Under-running of whole of sole and wall extending forward to toe

respond well to footbathing. If many of the lame sheep have scores of four, the outbreak is described as 'virulent' and requires more 'aggressive' treatment (though this does NOT mean extensive paring) – see below.

TREATMENT

The following methods of treatment are available, and the decision about which method or combination of methods is used will depend on the particular flock circumstances. It is important to realize that, in order to be successful, all infected sheep must be treated, with treatment being repeated until a cure has been obtained. If only obviously lame ones are picked out, there will be plenty of other animals with milder disease that will progress, and the disease will continue to spread through the flock.

Separation of Infected and Uninfected Animals.

Uninfected animals should be footbathed and then put on pasture not grazed by sheep for at least two weeks to prevent re-infection.

Infected animals should be managed as a separate group and only reintroduced to the healthy group when you are sure they have recovered.

Trimming

The view that feet should be pared hard 'to let the air in' is not tenable on welfare grounds. For optimum effect observe the following procedure:

● Trim only when the foot is significantly overgrown or misshapen, to identify infected feet, or to remove obviously loose horn prior to footbathing or other treatment.

● Do not cause bleeding, as this will cause unnecessary pain and can lead to granuloma formation (see Chapter 12).

● If an animal has severe footrot, do not trim immediately, but treat with antibiotic by injection (see below), then footbath in zinc sulphate. The feet of most animals treated with antibiotic injection will begin to heal, and loose horn can then be humanely trimmed away after a week or so, prior to another footbathing session.

Footbathing

Footbathing should preferably be in 10 per cent zinc sulphate with a stand-in time of 5–30 minutes depending on the severity of the disease. This should be repeated every five to seven days (see below). Success has also been reported by using a 15–18 per cent solution of zinc sulphate daily for five days, with a stand-in time of 10min. Walking slowly through 3 per cent formalin is an alternative, but should not

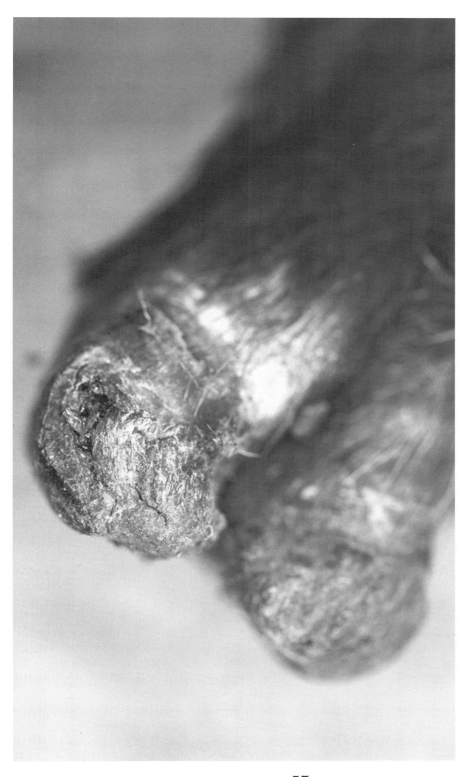

Chronically infected feet may not respond to treatment.

be used for severe cases as it is extremely painful. For optimum effect, observe the following procedure:

● If possible, treat on a dry day.

● If the feet are dirty, footbathing will be more effective if the animals can walk through a bath containing plain water first.

● If zinc sulphate is used, a few squirts of washing-up liquid can be added (this is not necessary if it is a proprietary product including a surfactant); this will speed the uptake of zinc into the horn. Zinc sulphate solution can be re-used as it does not deteriorate. Affected animals MUST stand in for the correct time according to the instructions on the pack – this may be as long as 30 minutes.

● If formalin is used, the strength should not be more than 5 per cent, preferably 3 per cent. Baths need to be made up freshly each time, as contaminated formalin quickly deteriorates.

● After going through the footbath, the animals should stand on dry ground for 30 minutes and then go on to pasture rested for two weeks if at all possible.

Antibiotic Spray –

The use of antibiotic spray is suitable for small numbers of early cases. Remember the following:

● Do not footbath as well as applying spray.

● Do not turn animals immediately back to grass, particularly if it is wet. Allow the spray to dry on the feet for at least 30 minutes.

● Repeat the treatment on several occasions at intervals of one to two days. A single treatment is not likely to be sufficient.

Antibiotic Injection –

Injecting with antibiotic is very helpful for severe cases. Observe the following procedure:

● Do not trim initially.

● Give an appropriate injection of antibiotic (see Chapter 5 and consult your vet). Remember the correct withdrawal period.

● Mark injected sheep, and keep them as a separate group.

● Footbath with zinc sulphate, but not with formalin (as is too painful).

● Check the feet after five to seven days; the feet should be much improved.

● Follow up by trimming obviously loose horn and footbathing as above, preferably in zinc sulphate.

Antibiotic Footbath –

These footbaths should only be used for confirmed CODD cases (see Chapter 9) that do not respond to other treatments. Although antibiotic footbaths are effective against footrot and scald, it cannot be good practice to use them where other effective non-antibiotic options exist. The possible long-term adverse effects, such as the development of antibiotic resistance, are unknown at this stage.

Vaccination –

Currently one vaccine is available, containing ten strains covering the common serogroups found in the UK. It can be curative as well as preventive. Before considering vaccination, make sure your diagnosis is correct (see Chapter 6), and also be aware of the disadvantages of the vaccine (see Chapter 5, and read the data sheet that comes with the vaccine).

Vaccination is definitely worth considering for a flock heavily infected with footrot. An improvement will be seen soon after the first vaccination, and a second vaccination given four to six weeks later should result in a marked reduction in the number of infected animals.

Do not give the vaccine to ewes within the period four weeks before lambing to four weeks after lambing. If given close to lambing, many of the antibodies will go into the colostrum and the ewe will not benefit. Nor will the lambs benefit, as the antibodies obtained through the colostrum do not protect for very long.

Whether to continue vaccination once good control of the disease situation has been gained will depend on individual flock circumstances – for instance, the risk of reintroduction of disease.

TREATING LAME PREGNANT EWES

Many shepherds do not like treating heavily pregnant lame ewes as they are afraid of inducing abortion through the extra handling. However, leaving them untreated means that the disease will spread to others, particularly if they are housed, and the ewes will be more likely to run into metabolic problems such as pregnancy toxaemia (twin lamb disease) because they cannot compete so well for food. The most practical solution is to treat with injectable antibiotic, but not to attempt to trim the feet at this stage. Trimming can be done, if necessary, a few days later. This should be done carefully, preferably by restraining the sheep against a wall and lifting the appropriate foot. Alternatively, turning a ewe carefully on her side should not lead to problems, whereas roughly grabbing a ewe and sitting her up on her tail may do so.

Inspection of the feet can be done after lambing, before turning out from individual pens. However, this will depend on the pressure of lambing and the availability of labour at that time. Remember that trimming dirty or infected feet and then going straight to assist a ewe to lamb is a recipe for disaster unless hygiene precautions are exceptional. The routine use of disposable gloves helps to maintain good standards.

SYSTEMATIC TREATMENT PLAN

1. (Vaccinate – optional, depending on flock type and the time of year).
2. Go through the flock and separate out the obviously infected animals.
3. Footbath the remainder of the flock in zinc sulphate or formalin (if a few animals with mild infection remain in this group it should not matter providing footbathing is done correctly). Always allow the animals to stand on dry ground after footbathing.
4. Put this group on to pasture that has not carried sheep for at least one, and preferably two weeks.
5. Continue to footbath this group at intervals of five to seven days, making sure that no new lameness cases are occurring. If they do, remove them to the infected group.
6. After three successive footbathing treatments, the uninfected group should all be sound, providing footbathing was done correctly. Continue to observe this group to make sure that they remain sound (see control measures below).
7. With the infected group, treat severely affected animals with antibiotic injection (after consultation with your vet). Mark these, and do not trim now.
8. Lightly trim the feet of the remaining infected animals only if they are significantly overgrown or there is obviously loose horn.
9. Footbath all, including the injected animals, in 10 per cent zinc sulphate with the correct stand-in period (likely to be 15–30 minutes). If you have to use formalin, do not footbath injected animals at this stage (too painful). After the requisite standing time, put them on clean ground if possible.

10. Re-examine the whole group in five to seven days. At this stage you can trim the loose horn of the injected group – their feet should have dried up, and the animals should be less lame.

11. Footbath the whole group again in zinc sulphate if possible. If you have had to use formalin, the injected group can be footbathed at this stage.

12. Repeat examination and footbathing after a further five to seven days. By this stage, many of the group should be cured and can be returned to the main flock.

13. Any lame animals remaining can go through the treatment cycle again, but if they remain lame they should not rejoin the main flock and you should consider culling them.

If a faster result is required, it is worth considering using a 15–18 per cent zinc sulphate solution (1kg to 7.5ltrs water) daily for five days, with a stand-in time of 10 minutes to treat infected animals. This is obviously more labour-intensive, but it may produce a dramatic improvement in the lameness status of the flock. Treated sheep should be kept separate from the rest of the flock until you are satisfied that they are cured.

Having successfully treated a lame flock, the next step is to maintain control over the disease in the future. As an alternative for self-contained flocks, eradication is a possible goal, but for most commercial flocks where replacements are regularly purchased, keeping a high degree of control is a more practical policy goal.

CONTROL

Many shepherds spend a lot of time and energy going through flocks carrying out 'routine' foot trimming, yet never succeed in gaining real control over footrot. This is usually because treatment is not applied sufficiently rigorously, therefore the disease continues to spread through the flock. Treating only obviously lame sheep will never result in adequate control; however, you should also bear in mind that 'routine' foot trimming may actually make the lameness situation worse for the following reasons:

● Gathering sheep can help to spread footrot infection if pens are dirty and poorly maintained.
● Footbathing is not carried out at all following trimming, or, if done, is not done correctly. The most obvious failures are in incorrect preparation of footbath solutions (too weak and they are ineffective, too strong and the formalin can excessively harden and damage the feet) and, in the case of zinc sulphate, insufficient stand-in time.
● Overtrimming can damage the feet, leading to granuloma formation and chronic lameness.
● Foot trimmings from infected sheep can remain infectious for several days and can infect other animals subsequently passing through the pens.
● If there is no suitable hard standing area for treated sheep – it is a waste of time and effort to turn sheep immediately back on to wet or long grass.

Other factors that lead to poor control are:

● failure to cull chronically infected animals;
● the introduction of newly purchased stock (including rams) without checking foot health;
● poor fencing, allowing in neighbours' sheep that may be infected.

Successful Control

The main thing to grasp about successful control is that, once you get on top of the disease by following the guidelines given earlier for treatment, and providing the flock is regularly inspected, the number of new cases can be kept at a low level. New cases are then caught at an early stage in the disease process, where footbathing alone will be successful in curing almost all – therefore there is no need for 'routine' foot trimming, other than to correct grossly overgrown feet (there will usually be some of these, even if a flock is footrot-free).

Successful control is therefore made up of the following actions:

1. Institute a correct treatment plan to reduce the number of infected sheep to a minimum. This is most easily started after weaning when the size of the ewe flock is at its lowest and the weather is most likely to be good, but treatment should not be delayed if a problem develops at another time of year.
2. Cull sheep that do not respond to repeated treatment or have chronically misshapen feet. These will be a constant risk to the remainder of the flock (see below).
3. Consider if an on-going vaccination policy is necessary. This will depend on flock circumstances, for instance, if it is impossible to gather easily, or animals are being sent away to better grazing.
4. Quarantine any bought-in sheep (including rams). Examine the feet of all bought-in animals, and separate and treat any that are infected, as instructed above. (There are many other important reasons for quarantining newcomers.)
5. Footbath the remainder of the bought-in group at least three times at intervals of five to seven days, and recheck for lame ones before mixing with resident sheep.
6. Keep a regular check on the whole flock, and investigate any increase in lameness before it gets the chance to get out of hand.
7. Pay special attention to foot soundness if animals are to be sent away for grazing

or are soon to be housed. Keep back any sheep that do not respond to treatment.
8. Footbath adequately before sending away or housing.
9. Don't neglect the rams – these can easily be forgotten.

Chronically Infected Animals

Animals that fail to respond to several treatment cycles, including antibiotic injection and footbathing, and those that have chronically misshapen feet, are a danger to the rest of the flock. As a last resort, you could try footbathing for one hour in 15 per cent zinc sulphate repeated daily for five days. (Do not use formalin or the horn will become excessively hardened, leading to other problems). If this fails, these animals pose a problem, particularly if they are of specific genetic value in a pedigree flock; the best advice is not to keep them, but if you really must:

● Keep them as a separate group
● Don't leave the rams in with the ewes any longer than necessary, and make sure the rams have not become infected when you remove them – examine and footbath thoroughly
● Wean any lambs as early as possible and make sure their feet are uninfected before putting with others

The first major problem is, how do you legally cull lame animals? Lame animals – identified as those that cannot stand on all four legs – cannot be legally transported, and definitely cannot be presented at market. The options are either, to kill on the farm and dispose of the carcasses legally – to a knacker or hunt if available in the district, or via the Fallen Stock Scheme; or if not too severely lame, speak to the official veterinary surgeon at the nearest slaughterhouse that takes sheep – explain the problem and see if the animals can be taken direct for slaughter. If you are in doubt about what is the best course of action, contact your vet for advice, or speak to your local DEFRA office.

ERADICATION OF FOOTROT

This is the ultimate step for self-contained flocks where no animals are bought in. Although it can be hard work to achieve footrot-free status, it is very rewarding to do so. There are a few facts to bear in mind before setting out on this final step:

● Freedom from footrot is not the same as freedom from lameness – there are many other causes of lameness
● Self-contained means ABSOLUTELY no animals added. Beware the occasional purchased ram; any threat from straying sheep; the possible risks from showing sheep and the risks if sheep are taken to market and not sold
● It is not worth considering eradication if boundary fences are not sound or if you use any common grazing
● If a ram is to be brought on to the farm, check feet thoroughly then footbath in 10% zinc sulphate and quarantine for three weeks. During this time the feet should be rechecked and footbathing repeated at weekly intervals.

Carrying out an eradication plan means applying the treatment and control measures already described, but more rigorously. Remember to use the correct concentration of chemical for the correct time, and stand the sheep on dry ground for 30 minutes after each treatment session. The essentials components are as follows:

1. Vaccination can be used to get a bad situation under control, but when going for eradication, it is best not to vaccinate so as to get a true picture of which sheep are infected.
2. Examine every foot of every animal.
3. Separate into infected and uninfected groups.

Uninfected group

4. Footbath uninfected group at intervals of five to seven days, rechecking that no infected animals have been missed. Move any suspect animals to the infected group.
   5. Put animals on clean ground (not grazed by sheep for at least two weeks) after each footbathing session.
6. After three sessions these animals' feet should all be healthy, even if the occasional slight infection was missed in the initial screening, as the repeated footbathing should have dealt with this possibility.

Infected group

7. Keep the infected group separate at all times. Always put through the handling system after the uninfected group, and clean and disinfect pens after these sheep have been through.
8. Lightly trim overgrown or loose horn.
9. Treat the infected group by correct footbathing. Badly infected animals should be treated with injectable antibiotic in addition (it may be worth considering using the relatively expensive drug tilmycosin at this stage, but consult your vet).
10. Re-examine after five to seven days. Footbath all again, and inject any that are still infected with another dose of antibiotic.
11. Re-examine after a further five to seven days. By this time, most should be cured. Check carefully, footbath, then add cured ones to uninfected group.
12. Any that have failed to respond to treatment or have misshapen feet should be culled as soon as possible.

13. Maintain biosecurity precautions strictly to make sure infection is not accidentally reintroduced into the flock.

14. Keep a careful watch on the flock, and examine any lame sheep as soon as possible. See pages 122–3 for a diagrammatic summary of steps in an eradication plan.

If a rapid result is required, the daily use of 15–18 per cent zinc sulphate to footbath infected sheep can be adopted, as described earlier.

SUMMARY

Summary of suitability of various measures discussed above for the treatment and control of both scald and footrot:

BREEDING FOR RESISTANCE TO FOOTROT

Experimental work has shown that some individual animals are naturally resistant to footrot. It is also possible that certain breeds may be more resistant than others, although it is difficult to find research work substantiating such claims. Breeding for natural resistance is a possible long-term method by which the national incidence of footrot could be reduced, but there would need to be a lot of research work to develop the actual methods by which this could be carried out.

	Scald		**Footrot**	
	Treatment	*Control*	*Treatment*	*Control*
Trimming	No	No	Yes, with care	No
Antibiotic spray	Yes*	No	Benign only	No
Antibiotic injection	No	No	Yes, if severe	No
Footbath	Yes*	Yes	Yes	Yes
Vaccination	No	No	Yes	Yes

* not both together

9 Contagious Ovine Digital Dermatitis (CODD)

This disease was first reported in 1997 and was at first called 'new virulent footrot'. It soon became clear that the clinical picture and response to treatment differed from classic footrot. Early work seemed to show the involvement of bacteria similar to those found in digital dermatitis in cattle, so the disease was renamed 'contagious ovine digital dermatitis' or CODD. Since first being identified, the disease has been seen in a number of flocks throughout the country. It is particularly nasty, and is difficult to eliminate when it gets into a flock; therefore every attempt should be made to see that it is not introduced into uninfected flocks by letting biosecurity precautions slip.

CAUSE

More work is needed to be sure about the exact cause, but that done so far has identified particular bacteria called spirochetes in many of the samples examined. These are similar to the type of bacteria called treponemes found in digital dermatitis in cattle, and those causing gingivitis (gum disease) in man.

DIAGNOSTIC FEATURES

The initial ulcerated, bleeding lesion occurs at the coronary band, and there is usually no interdigital inflammation, at least initially. The infection spreads

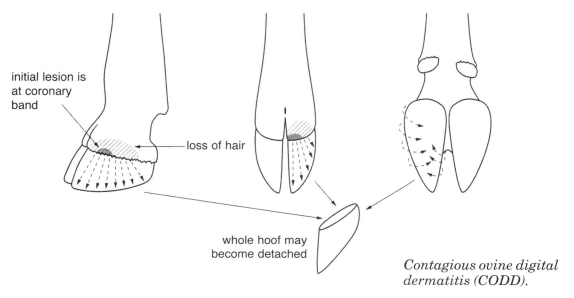

initial lesion is at coronary band

loss of hair

whole hoof may become detached

Contagious ovine digital dermatitis (CODD).

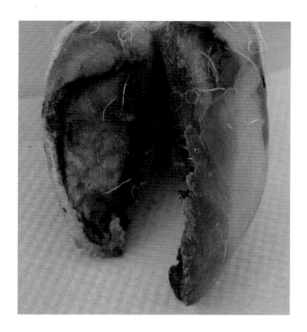

The first claw trimmed.

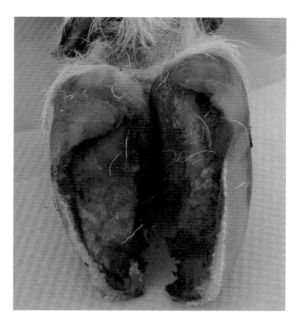

Both claws trimmed. Note the slight rotation of the lateral wall of the claw on the right.

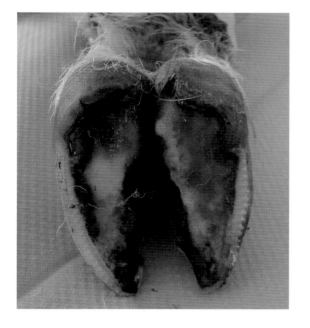

The second foot trimmed, leaving well-shaped claws.

The trimming of both feet completed.

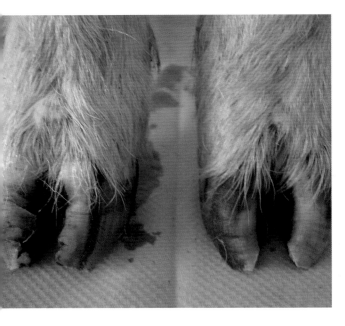

The front view of the trimmed feet. A slight crack remains in the wall of the claw on the left.

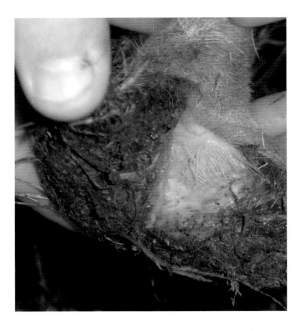

Scald, showing typical appearance of interdigital space.

Footrot showing an area of separation starting from the interdigital (axial) side of the claw.

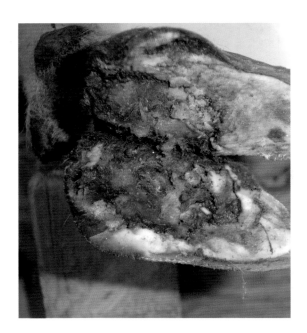

Footrot with an under-run area of sole exposed.

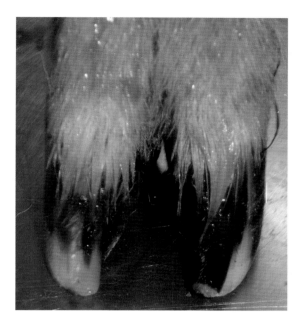

Excellent foot shape.

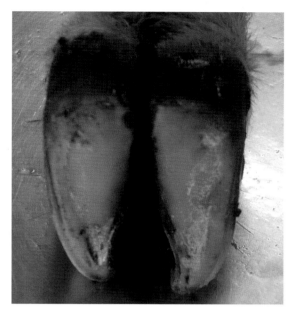

Good quality, even-sized soles of claws.

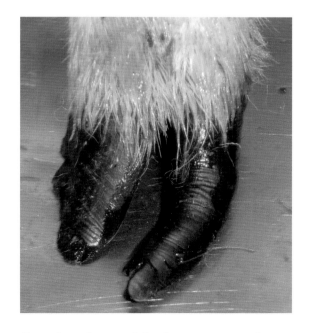

Poor foot shape with a long, narrow claw.

Poor foot shape with both claws showing abnormal rotation.

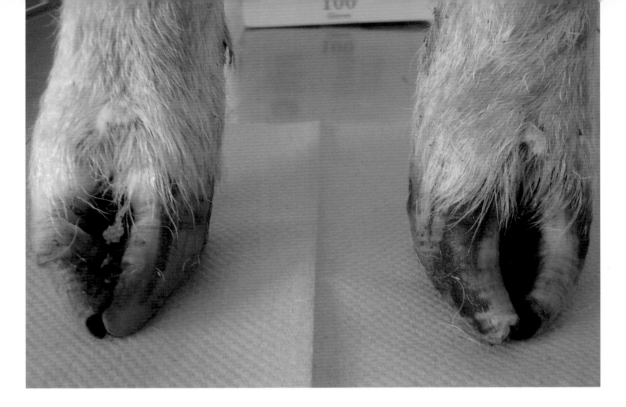

Front feeet with moderate overgrowth of all claws.

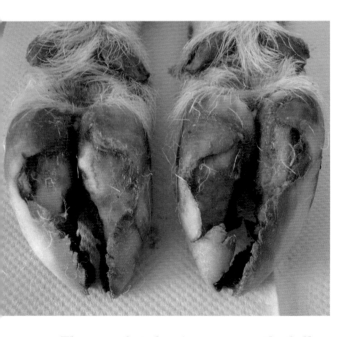

The same feet showing overgrowth of all claws.

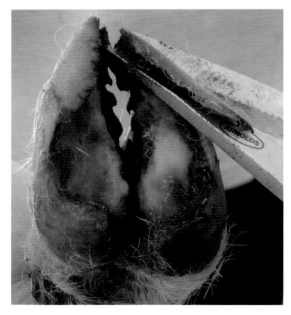

Trimming the first claw using foot shears.

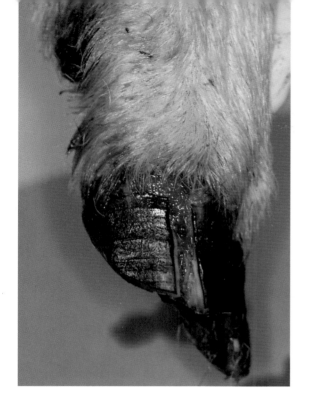

Slaughterhouse specimen with under-run wall as a result of white line abscess (do not trim in this way in the live animal!).

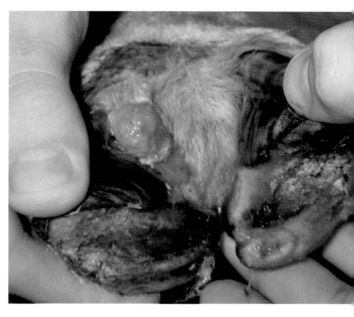

Acute pedal-joint abscess with granulation tissue surrounding the sinus in the interdigital space.

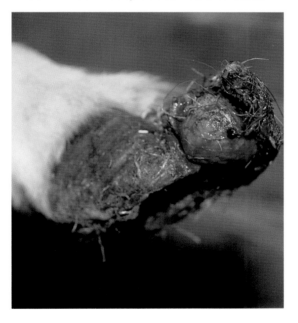

A toe granuloma.

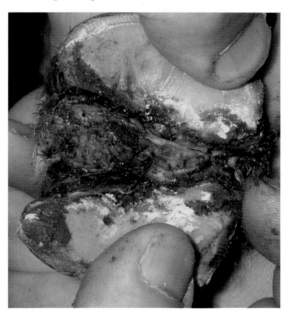

Interdigital hyperplasia with scald infection.

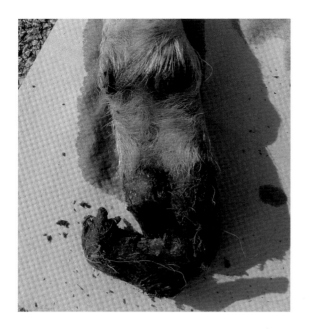

Soil-, or manure-balling.

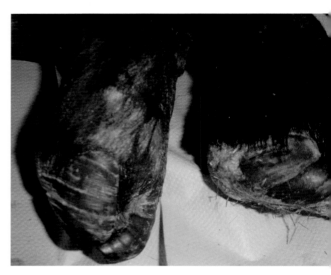

The front feet of a ram with severe laminitis.

Chronic erysipelas infection - note the swollen knees and signs of prolonged recumbency.

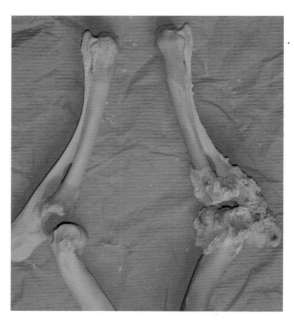

Osteoarthritis of one elbow joint. The other is little affected.

Antibiotic spray has been used to treat these feet affected with footrot, but will it be sufficient?

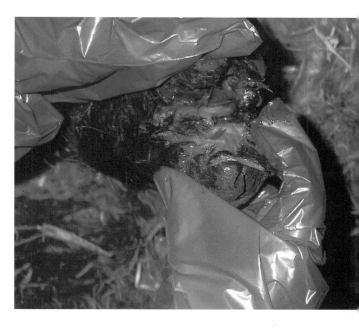

Severe footrot, which responded well to antibiotic injection.

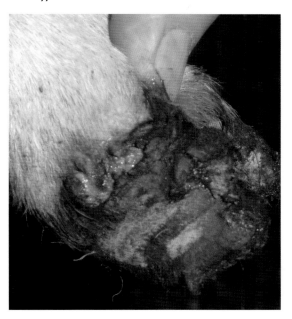

CODD showing lesion at coronary band.

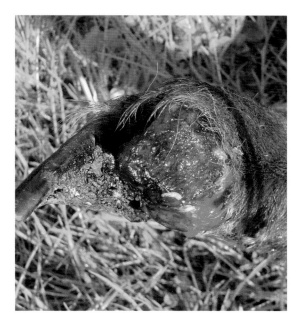

CODD showing whole horn capsule shed.

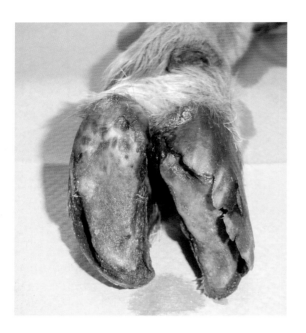

White line degeneration on the left claw showing the pocket formed under the hoof wall.

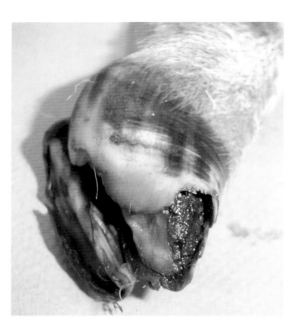

Extensive white line degeneration (shelly hoof).

Under-run area in the abaxial area of the sole, following an abscess in the white line.

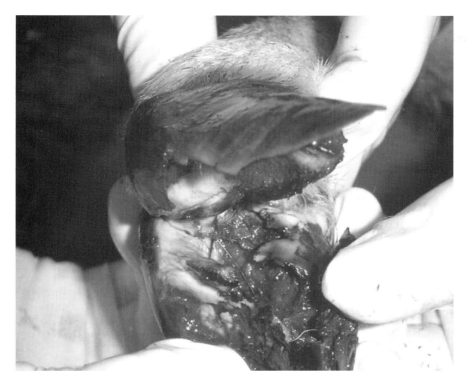

A CODD lesion separates the horn from the coronary band downwards.

A CODD lesion that almost completely separated the whole hoof.

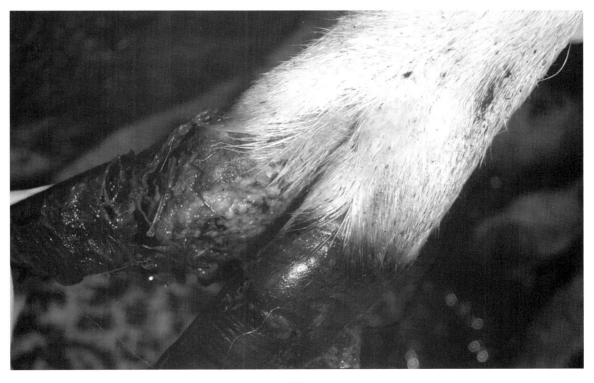

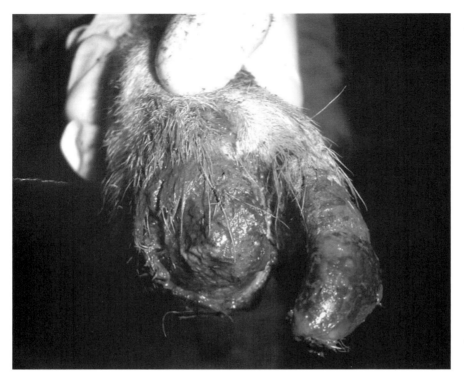

A CODD lesion with loose hoof removed.

This slaughterhouse specimen shows a permanent damage as a result of CODD.

rapidly down the claw, separating the horn from the underlying sensitive tissues so that the whole horn capsule can become detached. One or both claws may be involved on one or more feet. Affected animals are extremely lame. In really severe cases, the claw can be so badly damaged that the horn never grows back, although many do recover, particularly if treated in good time. Another common feature is that the hair of the skin just above the hoof is often lost.

Diagnosis may be complicated by the fact that most flocks in which this infection has occurred have also had virulent footrot too, so a very confused clinical picture may result. I have seen cases where I was uncertain as to whether we were dealing with CODD, virulent footrot, or both, but examination of a good number of animals will usually produce some with the characteristic early coronary band lesions if CODD is present. It is always advisable to get your vet to examine some affected sheep if you have a lameness problem that looks different from what you have seen previously, or if it fails to respond to normal treatments.

TREATMENT

Treatment of flocks infected with this condition should be taken seriously, as affected animals are a major welfare concern. Orthodox footrot treatments such as footbathing in formalin (don't try it for this! – it causes too much pain) or zinc sulphate have usually given poor results, as has injecting with antibiotics such as oxytetracycline or a penicillin/streptomycin combination. However, with a new outbreak, it is worth testing zinc sulphate footbath and injectable antibiotic on a few animals first to see if they are effective before resorting to other, more expensive or unlicensed treatments. If these fail to work, consult your vet about other options. These are likely to be:

● Injecting with tilmycosin, a relatively expensive antibiotic. (Remember the possible hazards of accidental self-injection – see Chapter 5).

● Footbathing in antibiotic solution – lincomycin/spectinomycin soluble or tylosin soluble have both been used successfully at a rate of 100g to 100ltr of water. This is an expensive procedure if a full footbath is to be made up for all the sheep, so some people economize by making up small quantities and applying to infected animals by spray, or by dipping feet individually in a small container. Whilst three treatments given at an interval of twenty-four hours will often cure the treated individual animals, it will not stop the disease spreading to others. It is likely to be necessary to footbath the whole group or flock in order to get proper control of the condition. (Disposal of antibiotic footbath solutions is a problem, as previously highlighted in Chapter 5.)

● Trimming away loose horn once recovery is under way.

CONTROL AND PREVENTION

Little, if anything, is known at present about how this disease spreads within a flock, or where, or for how long the bacteria survive. Because of the serious nature of the disease, it is best to try to eliminate it from a newly infected flock by a concerted effort of footbathing all animals, combined with treatment of those actually infected with tilmycosin injection; but always consult your vet to see if there is any more recent advice since this book was written. The most important message is not to get it in the first place! If you have to buy animals in:

● do not buy groups that contain obviously lame animals;

● isolate on arrival (this should now be normal practice);

● quarantine for at least three weeks;

● check feet for any sign of lameness;

● footbath as described previously for footrot control (I do not advocate footbathing in antibiotic solution as a routine measure);

● if any sheep develop foot lesions that you do not recognize, or which do not respond to treatment, seek veterinary advice.

Work is continuing on various aspects of the disease, so it is worth keeping up to date by watching for information in sheep or general farming journals, and asking your vet for any new information or advice.

10 White Line Lesions

The white line forms the junction between the horn of the hoof wall and that of the hoof sole (as described in Chapter 3). It consists of softer, more elastic horn than either the hoof wall or sole, and allows a degree of flexibility between these harder structures. It acts as a seal, theoretically protecting against infection, but because of its softer structure is easily damaged. In sheep, white line disease can take two forms: either extensive degeneration and separation of the white line along a part of the lateral wall of the hoof (sometimes called 'shelly hoof'); or a localized defect.

In shelly hoof, a section of the hoof wall becomes detached from the underlying laminae, forming a pocket that becomes impacted with mud and other debris. I have seen large numbers of sheep in some flocks showing this defect, even lambs of only a few weeks of age.

A more localized defect might appear as a black mark at one or more points along the white line (sometimes called 'toe abscess' if, as the name suggests, the defect is near the toe). This is seen more as an individual animal problem, with some animals repeatedly affected.

White line problems are commonly observed in some flocks during foot-

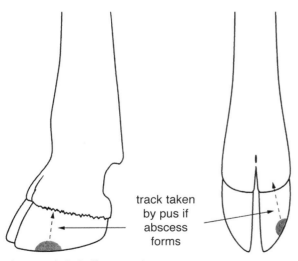

track taken by pus if abscess forms

characteristic half moon shape after paring away loose wall

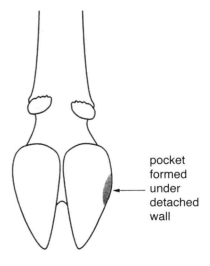

pocket formed under detached wall

White line degeneration (shelly hoof).

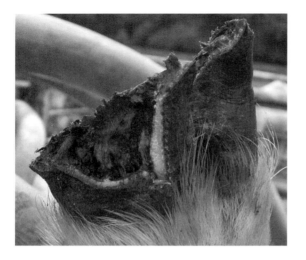

Extensive shelly hoof.

Shelly hoof with an abscess which has burst at the coronary band.

White line abscess.

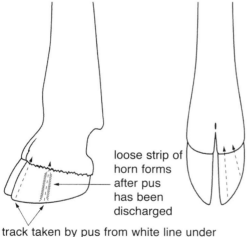

loose strip of horn forms after pus has been discharged

track taken by pus from white line under hoof wall to burst at coronary band

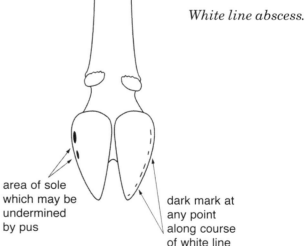

area of sole which may be undermined by pus

dark mark at any point along course of white line

trimming sessions, but do not cause lameness in the majority of animals. Lameness does occur when debris gets pushed through the damaged white line into deeper structures under the horn of the hoof wall. Once pus begins to form, the animal becomes acutely lame. Eventually, after several days, pus bursts out at the coronary band (the line of least resistance) and the animal gradually recovers. If the major infectious causes of lameness (scald,

footrot and CODD) are well controlled or eliminated from a flock, then white line disease usually becomes the most significant remaining cause of foot problems.

CAUSE

This is not known. Although white line degeneration and disease is seen

70

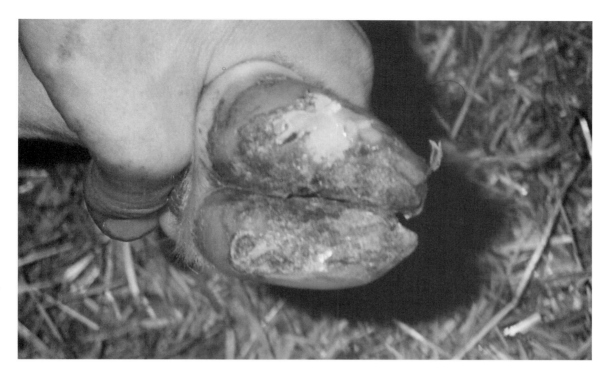

White line abscess pared to release the pus.

commonly in many flocks, it has not, so far, been considered to be a sufficiently significant problem in sheep to warrant time and money being spent on research into possible causes.

In cattle, white line lesions are very common and often lead to lameness. One major factor is thought to be excessive shearing forces produced when the animals turn sharply on concrete surfaces. This seems a reasonable theory for cattle that walk on hard surfaces at least twice daily during lactation, and are often housed on concrete for upwards of half the year; however, it is difficult to see that the same predisposing factor can be responsible for the problem in sheep.

Nutritional factors may also be involved. In cattle, supplementation of the diet with biotin (a vitamin) has significantly reduced the proportion of

animals with white line defects. However, this supplementation has to carry on for several months before a benefit is seen because of the time delay between new horn production and its reaching the position of the white line. There is some argument over what leads to the shortage of biotin. As this is manufactured by bacteria in the rumen of healthy cattle, one theory is that insufficient is manufactured in cattle suffering from subacute ruminal acidosis (SARA), which is a consequence of feeding too many concentrates in the early part of lactation. Whilst sheep are not generally recognized as suffering from SARA, ewes are fed increasing amounts of concentrates in late pregnancy, so it is worth considering whether there might be a connection with feeding.

Recent work in horses suffering from poor quality and discoloured horn in the region of the white line suggests that infection of the horn with certain bacteria and fungi may be an important cause,

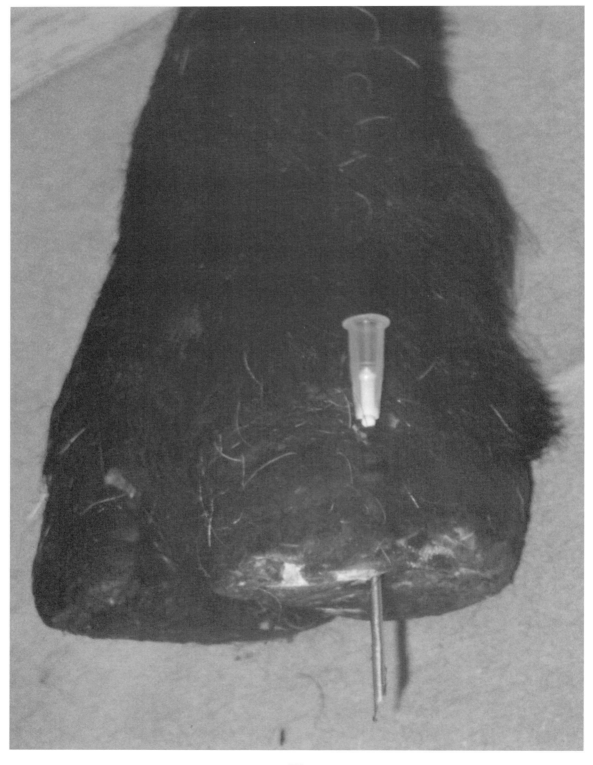

together with nutritional and managemental factors.

In sheep, it is possible that the localized white line abscess that sometimes causes repeated problems in individual animals may be related to a permanent defect in horn production from specific papillae on the corium, leading to a weakness in the horn produced at that specific site; but following on from the work in horses, it may be worth investigating the possible role of specific bacteria and fungi in damaging horn.

DIAGNOSTIC FEATURES

Extensive white line degeneration is easily recognized because of the pocket that develops under the detached hoof wall. When the loose wall horn is pared away, a characteristic 'half moon' shape, exposing the underlying keratinized laminae, is usually revealed. With the more localized white line defect, one or more black marks are visible when the sole is pared along the course of the white line.

It is important not to confuse these conditions with footrot. Sometimes the separation can be quite extensive, and if pus has formed, can also be smelly; but it should be easy to decide what you are dealing with because of the site of the lesion. With white line disease, the site of the lesion is at the abaxial (outer) wall of the hoof, rather than starting at the axial (inner) side of the claw as in footrot. The only time that confusion might arise is in late, healing cases of footrot where some detachment may remain along the wall towards the toe when the remainder of the hoof has been shed. Other, more characteristic footrot cases in the group will help in sorting out the diagnosis on a flock basis.

OPPOSITE: The needle shows the track remaining after the white line abscess has healed.

TREATMENT

White line problems are likely to be encountered in two main ways: as an incidental finding during general foot examination of a flock; and as the cause of sudden lameness in individual sheep when an abscess has developed under the wall of the hoof.

In the former case, careful paring of the loose part of the wall is all that is required. This will remove the pocket in which debris has become trapped, lessening the risk of an abscess developing. Do not pare any further once the separation peters out, and certainly do not pare so deeply as to cause bleeding. Footbathing in zinc sulphate or formalin does not appear to have any curative effect on the white line disease itself, but should be carried out if it is suspected that footrot is also present in the flock.

In the latter case, abscesses may be found in association with both shelly hoof and with the more localized white line lesions. The affected claw can be identified by gently squeezing each claw separately – the sheep will react by showing pain when the affected claw is squeezed. This claw will also usually feel hotter than the other, but there is rarely any significant swelling. Before paring the foot, check around the coronary band to see whether there is any sign of pus having already burst out, or a soft painful area where pus is about to burst. If pus has already burst out, it is best to leave the foot untouched rather than attempting to pare away the horn from around the discharging site. It is very painful for the sheep at this stage, whereas a few days later when healing has begun, it is usually possible to carry out some careful paring to lift away the under-run horn of the hoof wall. There may be some localized separation in the sole around the area of the white line defect, which can be gently pared at this stage. Again, do not confuse with footrot,

73

as the separation is on the outer edge of the sole, not the inner edge.

If there is no sign of pus having already burst, carefully pare the edge of the sole along the white line, looking for the tell-tale dark mark(s). Using a sharp knife, shave away the horn so as to follow the tracks into the hoof. Some tracks will peter out quickly and are obviously of no significance; others will continue deeper into the hoof. Sometimes the careful paring is rewarded by the sudden release of thin, pinkish-grey pus. This is the most satisfactory outcome, and the foot can be left to drain at this stage. The lameness should now improve, and if necessary, the claw can be trimmed a few days later to remove any obviously under-run horn.

More often, however, the track just looks a damp grey colour, with no satisfying run of pus. If blood appears, do not pare any further. Either leave well alone in the hope that pus will now work its own way out, or, if you wish to do more to speed things up, apply a poultice. This can be a special poultice material obtainable from your vet, or something as simple as some dampened bread or bran with a little salt added applied to the foot in a strong plastic bag. This should be firmly bandaged over the foot, though be careful not to cause a tourniquet-effect by bandaging too tightly. The poultice softens the horn, encouraging the abscess to burst, or making repeat-paring easier.

Remember never to pare so deeply that you cause significant bleeding. This type of abscess will always eventually burst by itself and the sheep will generally recover. Whilst this may take a few days, it may be better to let nature take its course rather than cause permanent damage to the foot by cutting too deeply if you don't really know what you are doing.

Use of Antibiotic

In the vast majority of cases where the abscess has already burst, I do not think it is necessary to give the sheep an antibiotic injection, as it will recover once the pus has drained. In cases where paring has failed to release pus, the decision is slightly more difficult. Experience has shown me that giving antibiotic may actually delay recovery, since the infection is suppressed but not cured by the antibiotic; thus the sheep may show a temporary improvement before relapsing again. As it is very rare for any long-term damage to result from this type of relatively superficial abscess, I now rarely advise giving antibiotic.

The main exception is in the case of a valuable pedigree animal when I would not take the risk, just in case this turned out to be the rare occasion on which the infection did not remain confined to under the wall only. You should consult your vet about which specific antibiotic to use, but it should be effective against a range of bacteria (broadspectrum) and should be long-acting, or a course of injections should be given covering several days.

After Recovery

When the infection has cleared and the sheep is sound again, it is worth re-examining the foot. You will usually find that a horizontal crack is present in the hoof wall, marking the point at which the pus burst; this gets carried down the wall as the new horn grows. Below the crack, you will often find a strip of horn that is now detached from the underlying wall. This is where the pus originally formed, and the strip can usually be pared away at this stage, leaving sound horn underneath.

An Alternative Treatment

Following the report of the successful treatment of hoof horn defects in horses, it may be worth trying the same treatment on affected sheep. However, this is only likely to be worth considering for valuable pedigree animals, since the treatment (a disinfectant containing a mixture of chemicals including an iodine complex, isopropyl alcohol and propylene glycol in tea tree oil) has to be brushed into the crevices of the hooves daily until healthy horn has grown.

PREVENTION OF WHITE LINE PROBLEMS

Since the cause is unknown, it is not possible to give any clear advice on prevention. The possibility of giving extra biotin in the diet could be explored, but because this needs to be fed for several months to show any effect, this is not going to be practical in most flocks. Sheep that suffer from repeated episodes of white line abscessation are best culled. In pedigree flocks, it would be worth investigating the family tree of persistent offenders to see whether there is any evidence of genetic susceptibility. Selection of breeding stock, particularly rams, should always take foot health into account.

11 Pedal Joint Abscess

The most distal bone in the leg is the pedal bone (third phalanx), which is almost entirely contained within the hard horn of the hoof. Moving up the foot, the next bone is the pastern bone (second phalanx) and between these two bones lies the pedal joint. At the back of the joint is a small bone called the navicular bone. The pedal joint capsule, which contains a small amount of joint fluid allowing these bones to smoothly articulate with each other, also lies almost entirely within the hard hoof, except on the axial (inside) side of the claw where it protrudes slightly above the level of the coronary band. This is relevant because it is vulnerable to damage at this site and if the joint becomes infected, it is also the site where pus will first burst out. Infection of the pedal joint is, fortunately, not particularly common, but when it does occur it is always very serious. It seems to be particularly common in heavy rams and ewes, although it can occur in any type of animal.

It is not always clear how infection gets into this joint. One theory is that infection gets in from an injury to the skin of the interdigital space – at the point referred to above, where the capsule is not protected by the horn of the hoof. Another possibility is that infection arrives at the joint via the bloodstream. It rarely seems to spread to the joint from a white line abscess (described in the previous chapter).

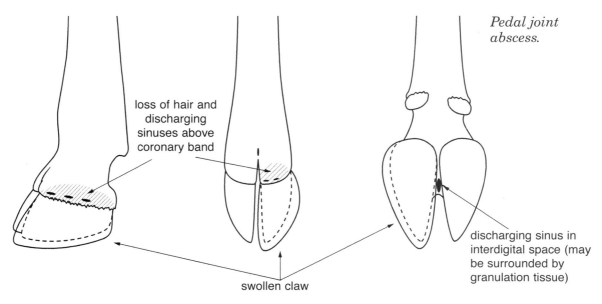

Pedal joint abscess.

loss of hair and discharging sinuses above coronary band

swollen claw

discharging sinus in interdigital space (may be surrounded by granulation tissue)

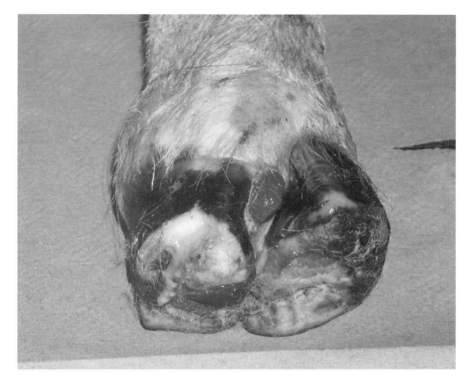

Acute pedal joint infection – note the swelling above the left claw and the granulation tissue marking the discharging sinus.

Severe lameness due to pedal joint abscess, with swelling above the claw.

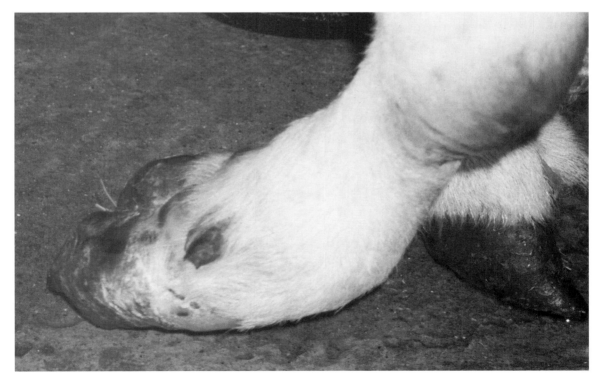

Whatever the route of infection, the outcome is the same – acute lameness with rapidly developing irreversible damage to the joint and usually to the pedal bone itself, leading to chronic lameness if untreated. Prompt veterinary treatment for an acute case may be successful in obtaining a satisfactory outcome, but by the time most cases are seen by a vet, the infection has reached the chronic stage and it may be too late to save the claw.

DIAGNOSTIC FEATURES

The usual sequence of events is as follows:

● Acute onset of lameness with the animal unwilling to put the foot to the ground.
● In the acute phase, the animal usually spends a lot of time lying down and often shows the degree of pain with increased respiratory rate and tooth grinding.
● The affected claw is hot and swollen and very painful to the touch.
● Discharging sinuses appear around the claw – first in the interdigital space, then at one or more places just above the coronary band.
● If untreated, the animal remains very lame, the claw becomes chronically thickened and enlarged, and poor quality, sometimes abnormal-looking horn is produced below the coronary band. Sometimes healing of a sort takes place with a lot of new bone produced around the area of the joint shown by the firm enlargement, but the sheep will always be lame to a greater or lesser degree. Sometimes the infection inside the claw is so severe that the pedal bone disintegrates into many sharp spicules of stinking, dead bone. This must be excruciatingly painful, and it is difficult to see how it can ever resolve to a situation where the animal can regain even some degree of ability to use the foot.

TREATMENT

These cases require veterinary treatment; administration of antibiotics alone is highly unlikely to result in a cure. If they are seen at an early stage, it may be possible to salvage the claw. However, most cases are seen by the time they have reached the chronic stage when it is usually not possible to save the claw. In the case of a valuable animal, radiography is helpful to determine the extent of the damage before deciding on the appropriate treatment. I must emphasize that the treatments described below are veterinary procedures only, which must be carried out under adequate anaesthesia.

Treatment of an Acute Case

Here, it may be possible to save the claw by draining and flushing the joint. Once clear of infection, the bones become fused (ankylosed) together so a functional joint no longer exists. The foot is anaesthetized, and a small drill is used to drill into the joint. A perforated catheter is inserted and bandaged in place and is used to flush out the joint. Antibiotics and pain-relieving treatment should be given. After a few days when the flushing fluid is clear, the catheter is removed and the claw re-bandaged. The lameness should improve over the course of the next few weeks as the joint becomes replaced by new bone. There is likely to be some residual thickening of the claw, but an acceptable result with minimal residual lameness may be achieved.

Treatment of a Chronic Case

Here, it is unlikely that the treatment described above will be appropriate because of the extent of the damage to the joint and pedal bone. The only way forward is either to have the animal killed on humane grounds, or for your veterinary

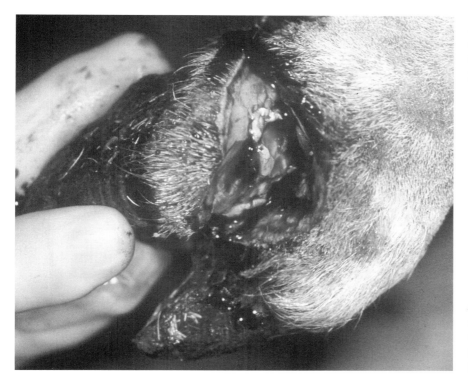

Amputating the digit – this is a veterinary-only procedure.

An amputated digit, showing the extensive infection in the deeper tissues.

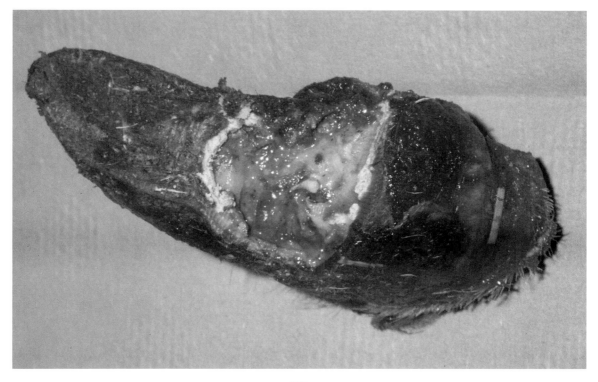

surgeon to amputate the claw. This is done under anaesthesia, with a tourniquet applied to the leg to prevent serious bleeding during the procedure. The claw is removed either by disarticulation between the first and second bones of the pastern, or by sawing off with an embryotomy wire. A firm dressing is applied to prevent bleeding – if this falls off within the first twenty-four hours, the animal may bleed to death.

The wound will require re-dressing several times, but usually heals within five to six weeks, although the sheep will be much less lame within a few days (surprising though it may seem because of the major surgery that has been carried out, but it is an indication of the severe pain the animal was suffering before treatment). It is usual to give antibiotics and pain relief at the time of the surgery. The length of useful life that will remain after the animal has lost a claw will depend on the soundness and conformation of the remaining claw and of the other feet, but usually at least one more breeding season should be achieved, and possibly more if the animal is well looked after.

PREVENTION

It is really not possible to give good advice about preventing this sporadic problem, since the cause is unknown. If the theory that the infection gains entry from injuries in the interdigital space is correct, care should be taken that the surfaces of yards and pens do not consist of sharp stones that can damage the feet. I have seen one flock that had several cases in rams, where the yard contained a lot of pieces of sharp slate, which may have been a factor in precipitating the problem.

12 Granulomas ———————

A granuloma is a piece of soft, very vascular tissue called granulation tissue, which is produced in response to injury. In sheep it is commonly found on the feet, often resembling a strawberry in appearance; when touched or cut, it bleeds profusely. (Excess granulation tissue is also a problem in horses when they have injuries to the lower part of the legs.) It occurs because the outer layer of the skin, or horn in the case of sheep's feet, does not grow fast enough to cover the wound before the granulation tissue, which is produced in response to injury and originates from the deepest layer of the epidermis, protrudes from the wound.

CAUSE

In sheep, the most common cause is trimming the feet too hard, especially at the toe, the most common site for

Granuloma.

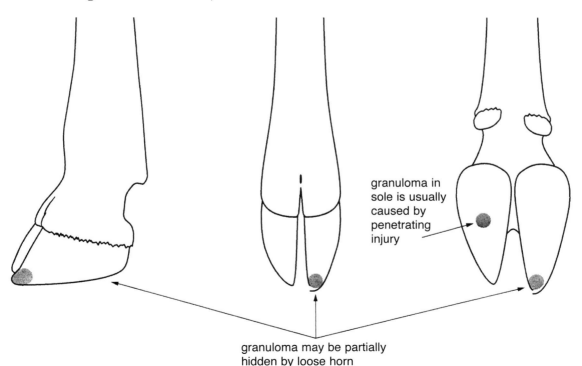

granuloma in sole is usually caused by penetrating injury

granuloma may be partially hidden by loose horn

81

ABOVE: Typical appearance of a toe granuloma.

Massive toe granuloma in urgent need of veterinary attention.

granuloma formation. Any trimming that causes bleeding is likely to result in growth of a granuloma, so correct trimming technique is very important. This is why it is better to avoid the so-called 'routine' trimming and only to trim carefully when the feet are grossly overgrown or misshapen, or to remove obviously loose horn before footbathing. Granulomas can occur in chronic footrot cases as a result of chronic irritation and infection of the corium, the layer beneath the hard horn of the hoof. They can also occur following accidental injury to the foot, such as penetration of the sole by a thorn.

Although some smaller granulomas may eventually resolve, the majority will not get better without treatment. They may become less obviously visible, as loose horn usually grows over partially hiding them, but if the horn is trimmed away and the granuloma cut off (causing profuse haemorrhage), it almost invariably grows again. Although granulation tissue itself does not contain any nerves, the corium to which it is attached is well supplied with nerves, so any pressure on the granuloma will cause pain. Affected sheep are therefore lame, although this may only be to a mild degree when the granuloma is protected by loose horn. The granuloma acts as an ideal site for footrot bacteria to colonize, so in a flock infected with footrot it is common to find both conditions co-existing.

DIAGNOSTIC FEATURES

Granulomas are generally easy to diagnose: they may be so large that they are immediately visible protruding from

Granuloma resulting from injury to sole.

beneath the hoof horn; others may not be obvious until the loose, overlying horn is trimmed away. They are usually pink in colour and bleed easily when touched.

TREATMENT

There is no point in simply cutting the granuloma off, as it will bleed a lot and re-grow. The options for treatment are as follows:

● Cutting off, followed by cauteritization with heat. This should be done by your vet, who will anaesthetize the foot in order to carry out accurate trimming to expose the base of the granuloma. After cutting off the granuloma at its base, a calf disbudding iron can be used to cauterize the area thoroughly, so that all bleeding points are stopped. If carried out correctly, the horn should grow over the defect and the granuloma should not recur.

● An alternative, slower method is to cauterize with copper sulphate crystals (blue stone); this can be done without anaesthesia. The horn overlying the granuloma should be carefully pared away, then some dry copper sulphate crystals applied to cover the granuloma, and a bandage put on to keep them in position. Remove the bandage every two to three days to check progress, and repeat the dressing with copper sulphate until the granuloma hardens (keratinizes) and can be safely pared away.

● Another method is to use 5 per cent formalin in a small container, applied every few days to the foot. This will cause the granuloma to keratinize, but it is risky because the formalin may excessively harden the hoof horn, leading to other equally serious problems.

PREVENTION

Although granulomas will continue to occur as a result of accidental injury, the vast majority are caused by over-trimming feet as described above. By limiting trimming to only those feet that are grossly overgrown and misshapen, carrying out trimming with care, and controlling footrot, it should be possible to minimize granuloma formation.

13 Other Foot Lesions —————

This chapter deals with a miscellaneous collection of causes of foot lameness other than those already described in previous chapters.

SOIL BALLING, MANURE BALLING

Diagnostic Features and Treatment

These are common problems in both outdoor sheep and housed sheep. In outdoor sheep, the cleft of the foot becomes impacted with a lump of hard, dried mud that often contains dead grass or even small sticks. In housed sheep, the foot becomes covered with a hard 'shoe' of dried manure and bedding material. In both cases, the diagnosis is self-evident. Once the offending lump of material is removed, it is common to find some infection of the interdigital space: this develops initially as a result of rubbing of the interdigital skin, which then becomes infected with the organisms that cause scald.

Treatment consists simply of removing the impacted material and applying antibiotic spray, or footbathing as for

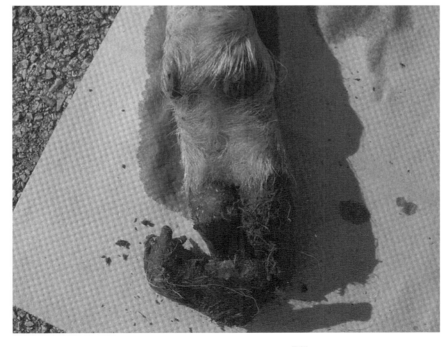

Soil or manure balling.

85

treating scald. Treating in this way is no problem when only a few sheep are affected, but if large numbers are involved it can be a real problem because it is impractical to handle all of them -- and in any case, the same problem can recur a few days later. For large groups, putting all the sheep through a plain water footbath may help to soften the lumps, or running them over an area of hard core or a mesh floor may result in at least some of the lumps becoming dislodged; then follow with footbathing to control the interdigital infection.

Prevention

With housed sheep, bedding quality is important. Inadequate amounts of bedding material or damp bedding is most likely to lead to this type of condition, whereas an adequate supply of clean, dry straw will help to avoid it. Using poor quality hay as bedding, or wasteful racks that allow a lot of hay to fall into the bedding, are likely to lead to this problem as a hay/manure mixture tends to become very 'claggy' and sticks easily to the feet.

With outdoor sheep, prevention is more problematical. The problem often occurs in autumn when there is a lot of dead grass in the sward, or in winter when wet weather leads to muddy conditions under foot. There is little that can be done in the way of prevention other than to practise good pasture management, so that the pasture remains well grazed and is not allowed to become too long, and to keep gateways and feeding areas in good condition.

INTERDIGITAL HYPERPLASIA (FIBROMA)

Diagnostic Features

This is characterized by the development of one or two outgrowths of skin between the claws in the interdigital space. These folds originate from the skin/horn junction, hence the reason that there are often two of them present in the foot, one from each side of the cleft. In a young animal these folds may not be apparent, but as it gets older the folds enlarge and become traumatized and infected. It is common for the skin on the sides of the folds to develop scald, so the animal becomes progressively lamer because of the mechanical effect of 'pinching' and repeated scald infection.

Treatment

If the folds are not too large, regular footbathing or spraying the interdigital space with an antiseptic foot spray should keep the scald under control and reduce the chances of any potential lameness. If the folds get so large that they are constantly sore, the only solution is either to cull the animal or to have the folds surgically removed by your veterinary surgeon. This will be done under local anaesthesia and the foot will need to be bandaged for a short time to control any bleeding. As this is a common problem in rams of some breeds, it is particularly important that these troublesome skin folds are dealt with well before the tupping season. At least two months should be allowed to make sure that the ram's fertility will not be adversely affected.

Prevention

It is not possible to prevent these folds developing in individual animals that already have this tendency. As there may be a genetic component, care should be taken in selection of rams and other breeding animals, particularly in pedigree or purebred flocks, so that there is less chance of passing on the fault to the offspring. However, as the folds can be

Interdigital hyperplasia showing two large keratinised skin folds.

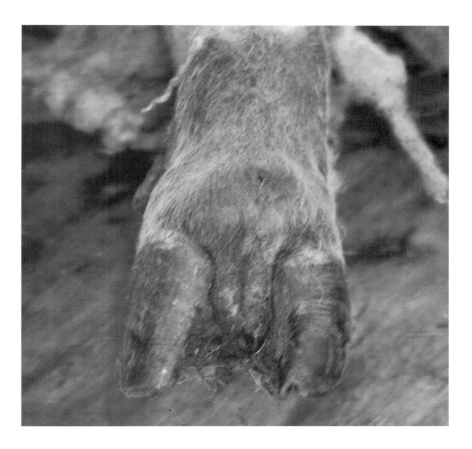

very small in young animals, the feet need to be examined very carefully to exclude their presence and, even after being careful in selection, there is no guarantee that they will not develop as the animal gets older. I would strongly advise against purchase of an adult animal that already had interdigital growths, since they will get worse rather than better as time passes.

FERTILIZER BURN

Sheep sometimes go lame following the application of granular fertilizer to fields, particularly if the weather is dry and the fertilizer does not quickly dissolve and disperse. Affected sheep show inflammation of the skin of the interdigital space, which, together with the history of recent fertilizer spreading, should lead to the correct diagnosis. Footbathing may be necessary to resolve the situation, which can be prevented by removing sheep from fields to be fertilized until after the granules have dispersed.

IMPACTED INTERDIGITAL GLAND

Background and Diagnostic Features

Sheep have several sets of wax-producing scent glands, one set of which is in their feet. Each foot has a single gland in the subcutaneous tissue just at the top of the interdigital space, with the opening of the

87

gland visible in the hair in the mid-line just above the hooves, often marked by a small plug of hard wax protruding from the duct. Occasionally the duct gets blocked and wax builds up within the gland: this becomes noticeable as an egg-shaped swelling just between the top of the claws. Normally this is of no consequence even though it can look a bit unsightly, but if it gets very large, it may make the skin protrude into the interdigital space where it can be subject to pinching by the claws, leading to lameness.

Treatment

In the majority of cases, leave well alone. Attempting to empty the gland by sticking a probe into the duct and squeezing to empty out the excess wax is usually not very successful as a long-term solution. I have never found it necessary to carry out any significant treatment with these impacted glands, although it would be theoretically possible to surgically remove them. Caution would be required, as it would be easy to accidentally damage the pedal joint capsule and end up with a much more serious problem; hence the advice not to interfere.

LAMINITIS

Cause

Laminitis is often associated with some generalized illness such as a difficult lambing, metritis (uterine infection), or acute mastitis. Another common cause is over-eating concentrates or starchy foods such as grain. Toxins produced by the bacteria associated with the acute illness, or from the upset digestive system, damage the microscopic blood vessels of the corium of the foot, blood flow through the corium is reduced, and the laminae and corium become inflamed, all leading to the extreme pain seen in affected animals. Another circumstance that I have seen lead to laminitis is in heavy ewes that refuse to lie down when confined to mothering-on crates; this is presumably because of the constant weight on the feet.

Background and Diagnostic Features

The fact that an animal has laminitis may be overlooked when it occurs as a result of another illness, and it may be some time before the damage to the feet becomes apparent. It is a potentially serious condition affecting all four feet, with the laminae and the underlying corium that produces new horn becoming inflamed. The animal becomes severely lame with all four feet feeling abnormally hot, and there is an increased pulse in the legs showing an increased blood flow to the feet. Normally it can be quite difficult to feel the pulse in the legs of sheep, but in laminitic animals, a strong, bounding pulse can usually be felt quite easily.

Affected animals are very reluctant to stand, and if forced to do so, usually take up a stance with all four feet tucked under the body in an attempt to relieve the pain. As a result of the inflammation in the feet, poor quality horn is produced, and this shows up as marked horizontal grooves in the walls of all the claws as the horn grows downwards. This poor quality horn is very prone to crack, with infection getting in under the wall of one or more feet, leading to the development of abscesses. These can develop some time after the original illness as the damaged horn takes several months to grow out, so episodes of lameness may occur long after the original cause has disappeared or has been forgotten about.

Good record keeping, with individual identification and accurate recording of illnesses and treatments, will allow checks

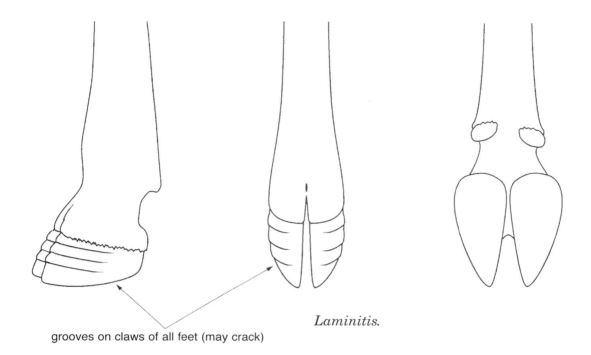

grooves on claws of all feet (may crack)

Laminitis.

Laminitis showing severely cracked hoof walls.

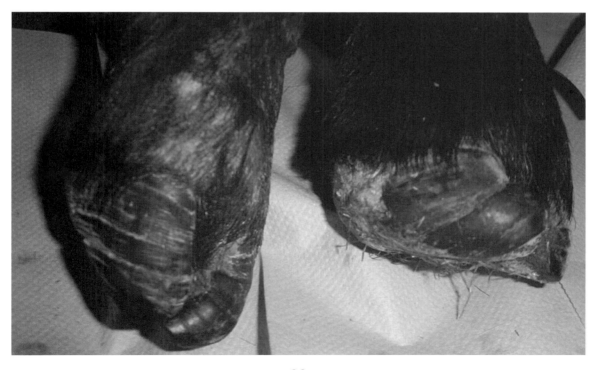

to be made on the history of affected animals.

Treatment

Severely affected animals may need to be killed on humane grounds. If treatment is not given quickly to acute cases and the underlying cause dealt with, the damage to the feet may be so bad that it is irreversible. Putting the animal on a thick, soft, warm bed such as peat, and administering pain-relieving drugs may help to ease the pain. If the underlying cause is successfully treated, recovery may occur quickly, but the longer term problem of the damaged horn will remain, and sporadic lameness incidents may occur that are associated with infection getting in via the weakened horn. These should be dealt with as described for white line abscesses (see Chapter 10). Regular examination of the feet and careful trimming of any loose or cracked horn until all the damaged parts of the horn have grown out may result in eventual soundness, but this can be a long-drawn-out process.

Prevention

By the nature of modern sheep farming and the lack of attention to individual sheep, sporadic cases are likely to keep on occurring. Prompt treatment of infections such as metritis and mastitis with antibiotics will help to reduce the occurrence of individual cases. Good management to avoid overeating of concentrates, either as a result of too rapid an introduction of concentrates to in-lamb ewes or fattening lambs, or accidental access to feed stores, will help to reduce the likelihood of group problems. Care also needs to be taken in feeding pedigree animals being prepared for show or sale, as it is easy to introduce concentrates in too high amounts, too quickly.

FOREIGN BODY

Background and Diagnostic Features

Foreign bodies such as sticks in the interdigital cleft have already been mentioned. Another form of foreign body is a sharp stone or grit that may have become impacted into a white line separation. Both these are obvious on proper examination of the foot. Other foreign body injuries may be from sharp stones or wire penetrating the sole, causing pain and introducing infection.

Treatment

This may simply be physically to remove the offending object from the cleft and to treat any soreness, or to carefully pare the white line to remove any impacted stones. With penetrating injuries of the sole, the original cause may no longer be present, but there will be evidence of injury and the associated pain, possibly with abscess formation. Treatment with long-acting antibiotic by injection is likely to be necessary. There may be some under-run horn to remove from around the injury site, particularly if an abscess has formed: do this carefully. Poulticing to encourage any pus to drain and to soften the horn may be necessary (see Chapter 10). Pressure can be taken off the affected claw by bandaging a thick pad of cotton wool to the sole of the sound claw. The outcome and timescale for recovery will depend on the exact site and depth of penetration of the sharp object. Seek veterinary attention if lameness persists or the claw swells, as this may indicate a more serious, deep injury.

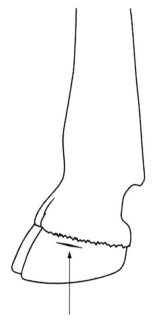

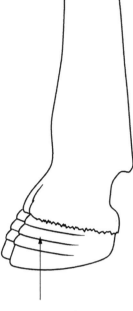

Horizontal cracks.

single crack on one hoof only follows healed white line abscess

one or more cracks on all hooves indicates systemic illness

BELOW: Vertical cracks.

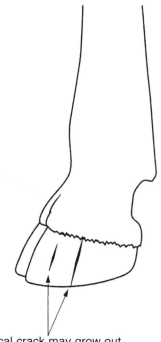

vertical crack may grow out or may remain permanently (sandcrack)

CRACKS IN THE HOOF WALL

Background and Diagnosis

Both horizontal and vertical cracks may occur in one or more claws. Cracking as a result of white line abscessation (Chapter 10) and laminitis (above) have already been mentioned; these both appear as horizontal cracks. Vertical sandcracks are not uncommon. These probably result from damage to the coronary band and may or may not cause problems to the sheep. If the crack is large leaving the hoof wall unstable, lameness is likely because of constant chafing of underlying sensitive structures and the possible entry of infection. With smaller cracks, whether

91

lameness develops will again depend on whether infection gains access.

Treatment

If the crack is small and does not become infected, it may be of no consequence and may eventually grow out. If pus has formed under the crack, careful paring, possibly after poulticing, may allow pus to be drained; but the problem is likely to recur unless the crack grows out. In horses with sandcracks, these can be dealt with by a combination of paring, use of filler to stabilize the crack, and special shoeing. Of course we cannot shoe sheep, but with a case in a valuable pedigree animal, it may be worth consulting a vet familiar with dealing with the condition in horses, who may be able to apply some of the same principles to treatment of the sheep.

FOOT AND MOUTH DISEASE

Background and Clinical Signs

A few years ago this disease would hardly have got a mention. Since the 2001 epidemic, and the fact that so much of the spread was via sheep, it must always be remembered that another similar epidemic could occur. Because of the current movement controls, it is to be hoped that any spread would be much more localized. One of the striking things about flocks that did become infected was the variation in the severity of signs, particularly the degree of lameness and how sick the animals appeared to be. In some flocks, the signs were fleeting and little evidence of lameness beyond the normal expected was noticed; in others, animals were obviously ill and reluctant to move. The main diagnostic features are the development of fluid-filled vesicles around the coronary bands of the feet and in the mouth, which soon rupture leaving raw, ulcerated areas. If a group of sheep shows any unusual signs of illness and increased lameness, the possibility of FMD should always be borne in mind. If in any doubt, always call the local DEFRA veterinary office for advice.

14 Lameness in Young Lambs

In contrast to the problems causing lameness in adult sheep, which, as we have seen, mainly originate in the foot, lameness in young lambs mostly originates elsewhere in the leg. The cause of some cases may be obvious (a full fracture with a swinging lower leg, or massively swollen joints), but in others – such as a partial fracture in the soft leg bones or the early stages of joint ill – a careful examination of the leg may be necessary before a diagnosis can be made. Starting at the foot, feel carefully up the leg, comparing the lame leg with the opposite one. Any swollen or painful area should then become more obvious. Check particularly the joints, again comparing those on opposite legs, and if unsure, compare with those of an unaffected lamb. Very swollen joints should be easily detected, but slight swelling can be difficult to pick up unless you are experienced or carry out a meticulous examination. One point to be aware of with newborn lambs is that, at birth, the feet are very soft and have a membrane or 'slipper' of soft horn attached to each claw. This is normal, and they rapidly wear off as soon as the lamb begins to walk.

The most common causes of lameness in the age group covering from birth to about six weeks are described below.

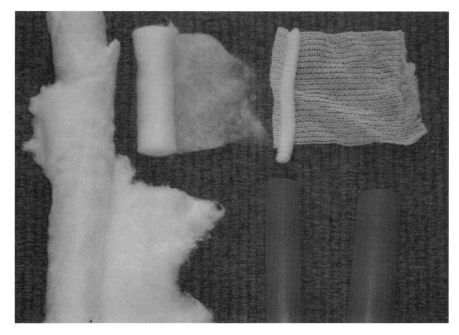

Splints, padding and bandages suitable for splinting the legs of young lambs.

FRACTURES

Background and Treatment

Fractures are common in young lambs, mainly as a result of being trodden on by ewes in overcrowded pens. The long bones in the lower parts of the legs (the cannon bones) are the ones that get damaged most frequently, but they may not completely fracture because they are very soft at this stage in life. This type of fracture is called a 'greenstick fracture' and may only be detectable by the swelling and pain at the site.

Fractures of the lower part of the limbs, below the knee or hock, usually heal quickly and well. They can often be treated successfully by padding the leg well with cotton wool and applying a splint. Your vet will have ready-made splints, or they can be made from a plastic pipe or cylindrical plastic bottle cut to a suitable size. Great care must be taken that the leg is not damaged by insufficient padding, unprotected sharp ends of the splint, or bandaging that is too tight. Alternatively your vet can apply a plaster cast, but because lambs grow so quickly, a splint is often easier to take off for the regular checks necessary to monitor progress. Healing is usually complete within three weeks, but because of the lamb's rapid growth rate the splint may well need reapplication after about two weeks.

Fractures above the knee or hock should always be seen by a vet, since these are much more difficult to deal with. It may not be possible to stabilize the bones simply with a splint or cast and, in the worst cases, it may be that it is better to kill the lamb humanely on welfare grounds. A similar fracture in a dog or cat would require expensive fixation with pins, plates or screws, and this is rarely economically worthwhile for lambs.

This lamb with bow legs needs immediate attention.

OPPOSITE: This lamb with contracted tendons needs immediate attention.

LIMB DEFORMITIES

These deformities are quite common, particularly lambs born with contracted tendons: in this case the front legs cannot be properly straightened, causing the lamb to walk with one or both feet turned under so that weight is taken on the front of the fetlocks. It is important that these are dealt with in the first few days, as they become much more difficult to correct as the lamb grows, even if left for only a week or two; also the limbs are likely to become infected where the skin over the front of the fetlocks becomes rubbed and sore. Again, the use of well padded splints can be effective. These should be applied to the back of the legs, reaching from behind the elbow to the foot. Firm bandaging will help to straighten the legs and as soon as the lamb can stand on the tips of its toes, the splints can be removed. It is really important that the splints are well padded, since the pressure of bandaging can lead to severe damage at pressure points such as fetlocks and knees. Checking progress every day or two and re-bandaging as necessary is the key to success.

Occasionally lambs are born with, or develop, 'bow legs', where the front legs deviate outwards. Again, it is important that correction is attempted early, as it is often impossible to do anything once the lamb has started to grow. Here, some ingenuity with splints and bandages is needed. If in any doubt, get your vet to see the lamb.

With these types of deformity, it is good for the lamb to have to get some exercise, as this helps to strengthen and straighten the legs, providing support has been correctly applied. Putting the ewe and lamb in a small paddock will allow for this and guard against the lamb becoming separated from its mother.

FOREIGN BODY

Young lambs have much softer feet than adult sheep, so it is very easy for sharp objects to penetrate the sole of the foot. The most common are thorns, which cause lameness both directly, and indirectly by introducing infection into the foot. The offending thorn may be immediately visible, but may not be so readily detected if it has been driven right into the foot. It is always worth carefully examining the soles of the foot if there is no other obvious explanation for lameness, as only the head of the thorn may be visible. If present, the thorn should be removed and pressure applied to express any pus that has formed inside the claw. It is worth giving antibiotic by injection if the wound is infected in this way.

JOINT ILL

Otherwise known as infectious polyarthritis, this is undoubtedly the most common cause of lameness in young lambs, and occurs when one or more joint gets infected and becomes swollen because of excess infected joint fluid or even pus building up inside the joint space. Infection probably gets in via the navel in the majority of cases, spreading to the joints via the bloodstream. Those joints most commonly involved are the knees, hocks and stifles. Bacteria can also settle in the joints of the spine, with infection damaging the spinal cord so that the lamb is unable to stand.

The most common bacterial cause is *Streptococcus dysgalactiae*, although other bacteria are sometimes implicated, such

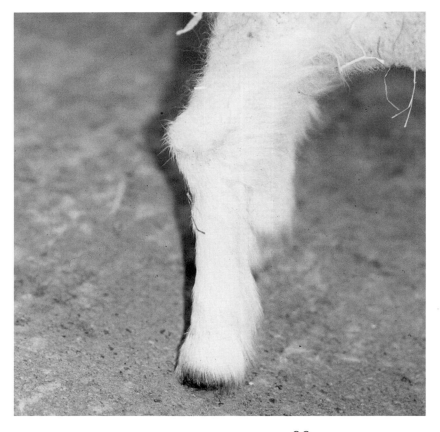

A lamb with joint ill – note the swollen knees.

as *Arcanobacterium (Corynebacterium) pyogenes*, *Fusobacterium necrophorum* and *Escherichia coli*, all common environmental bacteria. Occasionally the bacterium *Erysipelothrix rhusiopathiae* (that also causes erysipelas in pigs) is involved in disease in very young lambs, but since most cases of this become apparent only at several weeks or months of age, this particular type of joint infection will be dealt with in Chapter 15.

The disease is most often associated with poor hygiene in lambing pens, or where ewes are lambing outside in muddy conditions, though problems can occur even when hygiene is apparently good. Another important factor is colostrum intake by the lambs – too little colostrum, or, particularly, getting colostrum too late after birth, leaves the lambs vulnerable to infections because they haven't obtained sufficient antibodies to protect against common infectious agents present in the environment.

Diagnosis

This is easy if there is obvious joint swelling, but sometimes it is quite hard to detect the affected joint(s) in the early stages. If more than one joint is affected, the lamb may spend a lot of time lying, and may even be unable to stand. It is common to misdiagnose the problem as a muscle problem, white muscle disease (see below, page 101), at this stage. Careful examination should, however, detect one or more painful, possibly hot, joints with some distension of the joint capsule. Feeling and comparing the same joints in both legs of the suspect lamb may help to localize the seat of the problem.

Treatment

It is important that this is given early, since delay will lead to permanent joint damage and disability. Lambs that have

joint infections quite often have infections elsewhere – infected navels and liver abscesses are common. These multiple infections are unlikely to respond to treatment if there is any delay, and they may, in any case, be difficult to treat satisfactorily. Antibiotic injections should be given on the advice of your vet. It might be possible for your vet to open an abscess over a joint that is very distended with pus in order to flush all the infected material away, but the joint may already be severely damaged. In some other animal species, these joint infections are treated by inserting needles and flushing the joint out with sterile fluid, but this is a veterinary procedure and will rarely be economically viable for lambs. You must be prepared to accept that the most badly affected lambs may not recover and should be humanely killed.

Prevention

The key factors in prevention are as follows:
● Maintaining a clean lambing environment with plenty of fresh bedding, dry pens and regular cleaning of mothering-up pens.
● Adequate disinfection of navels. Strong (10 per cent) iodine is best for this, and should be applied to the whole length of the navel cord, since this is a common route of entry for the bacteria. Iodine teat dips as used for milking cattle are not suitable since these do not dry up the navel, which is the object of the exercise. The most effective method of applying the iodine is in a small cup, for example an old egg cup. A fresh solution should be used at regular intervals, and already used, potentially contaminated solution should never be poured back into the original container. Alternatives are the use of a spray to apply the iodine, or an antibiotic aerosol, but if these are used, special care has to be taken to make sure the whole

97

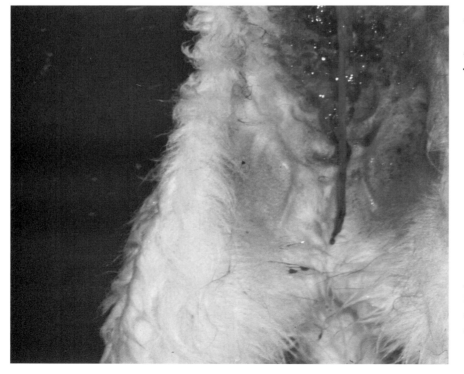

ABOVE: Dirty lambing pens predispose to joint ill.

It is important to thoroughly disinfect the navel of newborn lambs.

navel cord is treated. Remember that the ewe is likely to remove some of the dressing as she licks the lamb, so reapply if this happens. If there is a problem of navel and/or joint infections in the flock, it is well worth checking lambs' navels after twenty-four hours to see that they are dry and shrivelled. If not, re-apply some more dressing.

● Ensuring early and sufficient colostrum intake by lambs. This is vital in protecting lambs against infections of all sorts, not just joint and navel ill. Ewe colostrum is vastly superior to any commercial preparation (and cheaper) so try to make sure that all lambs from ewes with inadequate colostrum supplies get at least some ewe colostrum – 250ml is an absolute minimum volume, though a much larger volume is desirable.

In the face of a serious outbreak, consideration may have to be given to injecting all lambs with antibiotic soon after birth, but this is not a practice to be advocated unless absolutely necessary. You will need to take advice on this from your vet, as the best antibiotic to use may need to be based on the result of laboratory tests to identify the particular bacteria and their antibiotic sensitivity.

TICK PYAEMIA

Otherwise known as 'cripples', this is a well recognized type of joint infection specifically associated with lambs on tick-infested grazing. When the ticks bite the lambs, they inoculate the skin with a particular bacterium, *Staphylococcus aureus*, which normally lives on the skin surface causing no harm. At the same time, another type of micro-organism (rickettsia, that cause tick-borne fever) is introduced, and the effect of the infection with tick-borne fever is to severely reduce the circulating white blood cells that

A lamb with tick pyaemia; multiple joints are affected.

normally fight infections. This means that the staphylococci spread much more easily than in a healthy lamb: they get into the bloodstream and travel to the joints where they settle, and pus develops. The joints – as before, the knees, hocks and stifles most commonly – become distended with thick, yellowish pus and are generally permanently damaged, leading to the alternative very descriptive name for the condition, cripples.

Treatment

As with joint ill, treatment with antibiotic injection only has a chance of working if given very early, and since these lambs are generally out on rough pasture or hill keep at this stage, this is very difficult to achieve.

Prevention

Protection of lambs against tick bites is the primary aim. This is done by application of a 'spot-on' chemical, usually a synthetic pyrethroid, before the lambs are released to the tick-infested pasture. This is generally quite effective at preventing the disease, which is no longer as serious a problem as it used to be before the availability of these chemicals. If this method does not produce adequate control, it is possible to inject lambs with long-acting antibiotic as they are released on to the tick-infested ground. Long-acting oxytetracycline may be most appropriate, as this is effective against both the staphylococci and the tick-borne fever infection.

CLAW/FOOT ABSCESS

This seems to be a sufficiently well-defined condition, sometimes found in flocks without a joint-ill problem, to warrant a separate section. It mostly affects lambs within the first two or three weeks of life, and is commonly presented as acute lameness affecting one, and sometimes two, feet. Examination shows a very swollen foot, sometimes limited to one claw, but sometimes involving the whole foot. It is often possible to identify one or more soft areas around the foot where an abscess in one or more of the lower limb joints (usually the pedal joint) is coming to a head, or this may even already have burst, discharging yellowish pus. No particular type of bacteria has been associated with it, nor is the exact

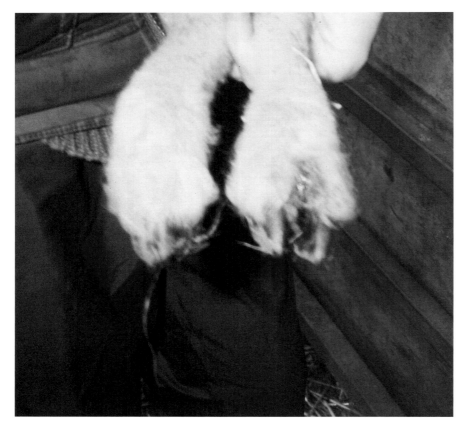

Foot abscess in a young lamb.

100

mechanism of how infection gets into the joints clear, but it seems most likely that infection has travelled via the bloodstream as in joint ill, but only settled in one or more of the foot joints.

Treatment

The main thing is to remove the pus as soon as the abscess bursts by bathing with salt water (add about a rounded teaspoon to half a litre of warm, previously boiled, water and use a plastic jug so you can place the lamb's leg in it). By squeezing the foot around the area of the swelling (this will be painful for the lamb but needs to be done), as much pus as possible should be expressed. This procedure should be repeated twice a day if necessary, although a couple of treatments are often sufficient. Antibiotic from your vet should also be given by injection. It is surprising how well these foot infections usually heal, and most lambs become sound again fairly quickly.

Prevention

Apart from the general precautions indicated for preventing joint ill, there is no other specific advice that can be given. As it is a sporadic problem only, it is unlikely that more than a small number of lambs within a particular flock will be affected in any one lambing season.

REDFOOT

This is an uncommon problem, though a significant one because it is probably hereditary, which becomes apparent within the first few days of life. Scottish Blackface sheep are most commonly affected, but it has also been reported in Welsh Mountains. Affected lambs have a (probable) genetic defect which leads to the deeper layers of the skin, the dermis,

separating from the more superficial layer, the epidermis. As horn is the equivalent of the epidermis, the hooves are affected and separate from the sensitive deeper structures of the foot. The hooves drop off, leaving the sensitive inner part of the feet exposed and unprotected. These then become infected and very painful, crippling the lamb. Other parts of the body, such as the mouth and nose, may also show ulcerations. As soon as the condition is recognized, affected lambs should be humanely killed as recovery does not occur. As it is considered to be hereditary, it is worth trying to identify which ram is implicated and culling him, although this will be difficult where groups of rams are run with ewes.

WHITE MUSCLE DISEASE

Otherwise known as nutritional myopathy, or stiff lamb disease, this is as the name suggests, a disease of the muscles seen in young, often fast-growing lambs. It may also sometimes affect lambs at birth, making them appear 'floppy' and unable to stand. The most usual presentation is that lambs of a few days to a few weeks of age, but sometimes older, appear stiff and have difficulty walking. Often, if being driven, they just lie down, unable to walk any further; after a few minutes they may recover and manage to walk a bit more, but some become completely recumbent. It is caused by a lack of vitamin E and/or selenium in the diet. Vitamin E and selenium are so called 'anti-oxidants', that is, they 'mop up' harmful substances called 'free radicals', produced during normal cell metabolism, that circulate within the blood and that can damage various tissues including the muscles. It is very easy to confuse this with joint ill, as emphasized above, so a careful examination is required to differentiate the two problems. Congenital

101

This lamb had nutritional myopathy – note the well muscled hindquarters and the atrophy of the shoulder muscles.

malformations of the legs may prevent a lamb standing, so check for these, too. These guidelines may help to distinguish between them:

● With nutritional myopathy, lambs are usually growing well and are often quite well muscled. The legs may feel stiff and difficult to flex because the muscles are stiff and painful, but there are no swollen joints.
● With joint ill, lambs often look rather miserable and may stand hunched up. They often look rather thin and careful examination should reveal one or more painful and swollen joints.
● Congenital abnormalities are obvious on proper examination.

These guidelines are not infallible and you will probably need to consult your vet in order to investigate further. It may be that blood samples and/or post-mortem examination of affected lambs are necessary. At post-mortem examination,

white areas or patches may be found in some of the skeletal muscles, although these are not always very obvious. It should also be noted that the muscles of the chest and heart can be affected, leading to difficulty in breathing or even sudden death.

Treatment

Lambs may respond well to an injection of a vitamin E/selenium preparation, although it may take several days before they can stand and move freely. If they are recumbent, it is important that they are confined to an individual pen with the ewe and are assisted to suck, otherwise they will starve to death or, if outside, get taken by a fox.

Prevention

It is important to know if there is a deficiency, particularly of selenium, as this mineral is toxic if too much is given, therefore it is not safe to supplement animals 'just in case'. Pregnant ewes need to have sufficient vitamin E and selenium during the later parts of pregnancy so that lambs are born with an adequate amount in the body. Most problems arise where home-grown feeds are relied on, as these will be deficient if the soil in which they are grown is deficient in selenium. Poor hay, some root crops, and grain treated with propionic acid will all have poor vitamin E content. Commercial sheep concentrates are supplemented with vitamin E, and animals fed these in late pregnancy are at less risk of this problem. There are several methods of supplementing ewes including various injectable preparations and oral boluses. These are usually given from about the end of the third month of pregnancy. However, because of the possible risks of selenium toxicity, a need should be established by involving your vet in a proper investigation before a decision to administer any of them is taken.

RICKETS

This affliction is now uncommon, as feeding standards in sheep have improved in recent years. It is caused by an imbalance in calcium and phosphorus in the diet, together with a deficiency of vitamin D. Animals most at risk are those housed in the winter, because of a lack of exposure to sunlight (vitamin D is manufactured in the skin in response to sunlight), particularly if they are fed poor quality hay. The leg bones become soft and bend under the weight of the body, and the affected animals fail to thrive. The clinical signs are usually diagnostic. A review of feeding will be necessary to determine the cause.

Treatment

Injecting with vitamin D will be effective in improving bone strength, though some bowing of the legs may remain. Overdosage with vitamin D is possible, so advice will be needed on treatment.

Prevention

Rickets can be avoided by improved feeding with a correct balance of calcium and phosphorus, and exposure to sunlight.

SWAYBACK

Swayback is a neurological problem, not a true lameness, but is included briefly here because affected lambs have difficulty walking. As the name suggests, the characteristic appearance of affected lambs is of weakness in the back and hindlegs, so that they walk with a swaying motion, or may even drag the back legs when they try to run. Lambs may be affected at birth, sometimes so badly that they cannot stand, or the condition may not become apparent until the lambs are several weeks old, in which case it is called 'delayed swayback'.

Cause

Lambs get swayback because the ewes have a diet deficient in copper during pregnancy. To be strictly accurate, the problem may be due to an excess of minerals such as molybdenum, iron and sulphur, rather than an outright deficiency of copper, as these 'mop up' copper in the diet and make it unavailable to the ewe. Certain areas of the country are known to have high molybdenum levels in the soil, so there will usually be local knowledge of this. Copper is essential for the correct development of parts of the nerves in the spinal cord and brain, so too little copper means that these parts either do not develop properly, or degenerate, and the severity of the clinical signs depends on the degree and site of damage present.

Treatment

As the changes in the nervous system are irreversible, treatment is not possible. Further deterioration may sometimes be prevented by administration of copper, but as this can be toxic, veterinary advice should be sought.

Prevention

Copper can be given to ewes in mid-pregnancy to prevent swayback in their lambs, but the whole subject of copper deficiency and toxicity is complex, so veterinary help should be sought to ensure a correct diagnosis before considering administration of extra copper by any route.

SPINAL ABSCESS

This condition will cause difficulty in walking, with progressive loss of use of the hind legs. It can sometimes be difficult to distinguish from swayback except by post-mortem examination and other laboratory tests. Spinal abscess may be a part of a wider joint-ill problem within a flock, or it may be related to infection gaining access from tailing wounds. There is no treatment, so affected lambs should be humanely killed.

This lamb could not stand because of a spinal abscess.

15 Other Causes of Lameness in Growing Lambs and Adults ———

In this age group there is a miscellany of conditions that result in lameness or discomfort, some affecting many sheep, others affecting individuals or small numbers only. It will usually be necessary to carry out a thorough examination of the affected animal(s) in order to be sure of the cause, and veterinary help may be necessary.

FRACTURES

As in young lambs, a fracture as the result of an accident can occur at any time. It may be obvious that the leg has broken in, for example, an animal attempting to jump a hurdle and getting a leg caught in it, or the incident may be unobserved. Fractures of the lower parts of the limbs (the cannon bones) usually heal well, providing the skin is not broken. These will need to be treated by your vet as, almost certainly, a plaster cast will need to be applied. Healing usually takes three to four weeks.

If the skin is broken (called a compound fracture) the outcome is less certain, as there will inevitably be contamination and infection of the fracture site. Take veterinary advice. Fractures above the knee or hock are, as in young lambs, much more difficult to deal with, and you will need to consult your vet and/or be prepared to humanely kill the animal on welfare grounds. Remember that it is legal to transport a casualty like this for veterinary treatment, but not to a slaughterhouse. If in doubt, seek advice.

FOREIGN BODY

Thorns can continue to cause problems in the relatively soft horn of the feet of growing lambs, as in young lambs (see Chapter 14).

ERYSIPELAS ARTHRITIS

This is a common cause of joint infection in growing lambs: the causal organism is called *Erysipelothrix rhusiopathiae*, the same one that causes erysipelas in pigs. It is also responsible for the separate condition called post-dipping lameness (see below). In erysipelas arthritis, the bacteria probably infect the lambs within the first few days of life and travel via the bloodstream to the joints, but rarely cause obvious disease at this stage. Instead, there is a gradual onset of stiffness and lameness as the joints become progressively damaged over a matter of weeks. It is common for lambs to reach six to eight weeks of age, or even as much as six months, before it is realized that there is a problem. By this stage, many of the affected joints have severe, irreversible damage, with erosion of the cartilage covering the joint surfaces, and fibrosis and thickening of the joint capsule. Affected lambs fail to thrive, show

Chronic erysipelas – multiple joints of this lamb are affected.

increasing muscle wastage, and spend a lot of time lying down. If forced to walk they may 'bunny hop', particularly if the hips and stifles are affected. Some joints, particularly the knees, hocks and stifles, may show obvious enlargement, but the swelling feels firm, not pus-filled as in some joint-ill cases.

Diagnosis can usually be made on the signs and age group affected, but this can easily be confirmed in chronic cases by sampling to test for erysipelas antibodies in the blood. In earlier cases, which may be more difficult to pick out because the joints are not grossly swollen at this stage, your vet may be able to take samples of fluid from inside the joints. The samples can then be cultured in the laboratory in order to try to grow the bacteria.

Treatment

Often, by the time it is realized there is a problem, the damage to the joints is so bad that no treatment is possible. These severely affected animals are a dead loss and should be slaughtered on humane grounds. They will not be fit for human consumption and cannot legally be transported.

If affected animals are spotted before they reach the irreversible stage, it may be worth treating and housing them to attempt to fatten them for slaughter. Penicillin is effective against this organism – but it is worth emphasizing again that, from both a welfare point of view and on economic grounds, treating is only worthwhile when the affected animals are identified before too much damage has occurred in the joints. You will need to consult your vet concerning the advisability of treatment.

Prevention

Once the infection has been diagnosed in a flock, it is too late to do anything about the current lamb crop, but it is possible to vaccinate the ewes to protect the next lamb crop. The vaccination schedule is two injections given approximately four weeks apart, with the second one given about three weeks before lambing. In subsequent years, a single pre-lambing booster dose is needed. Protection is via

106

the colostrum in the same way as lambs are protected against clostridial diseases.

As the bacteria are widespread in the environment, it may be difficult to prevent the disease without vaccination, but the usual hygiene precautions in lambing areas should be in place. It is also sensible not to house lambing ewes where pigs have been housed, or at least to thoroughly clean and disinfect if such accommodation has to be used. There may also be a connection with poultry and rodents – the disease has been linked to contaminated areas where game birds or turkeys have been reared, so lambing in this type of location should be avoided if other control methods are not proving to be effective.

POST-DIPPING LAMENESS

This disease is also caused by the bacterium *Erysipelothrix rhusiopathiae*, but as the name suggests, is usually, though not always, associated with dipping. As previously indicated, these bacteria are common in the environment, and the usual course of events in an outbreak is that dipping takes place over the course of more than one day. Sheep dipped on the first day are unaffected. The contaminated dip is allowed to stand (overnight may be sufficient in warm weather), during which time the bacteria in the dip multiply rapidly. The remainder of the sheep are then dipped in the same, now contaminated, bath. The bacteria get into the skin of the lower legs of the sheep through the inevitable grazes and small nicks acquired during the dipping process. A few days after dipping, a number of the sheep are seen to be ill, reluctant to get up and are found to have raised temperatures. The lower parts of the legs around and above the coronary band are hot, red and swollen.

The same situation may arise if a dip

bath has been prepared using water that has accumulated over a period of time, rather than discarding this and filling the dip with fresh water. A similar picture, not associated with dipping, has been recognized when sheep have been gathered and held for some time in very muddy pens, particularly in warm weather. In these circumstances the lower parts of the legs of the sheep get very dirty and wet, again predisposing to infection with these bacteria should they be present in the mud. You should also bear in mind that in some flocks infected with foot and mouth disease in the 2001 outbreak, a similar picture of illness, raised temperature and lameness was seen. If in doubt, seek veterinary help!

Treatment

These particular bacteria are sensitive to penicillin, and providing that treatment is given as soon as the problem and its cause are recognized, most affected animals should respond to treatment with this antibiotic. You will need to consult your vet to obtain an appropriate product.

Prevention

Dips should be cleaned out and filled with fresh water immediately before dipping is to take place, rather than using stale water that may have accumulated over weeks or even months. It is advisable to add a disinfectant recommended by the dip manufacturer at the beginning of dipping. Dip solutions should never be re-used after standing overnight unless a recommended disinfectant has been added. Dip manufacturers give advice about compatible disinfectants, and their instructions should always be followed. Erysipelas vaccine may be used if there is a persistent flock problem: the primary course consists of two injections about three weeks apart, followed by annual boosters a few weeks before the main risk period.

STRAWBERRY FOOTROT

This disease has nothing to do with footrot, and nothing to do with the toe granulomas sometimes referred to as 'strawberries'. What happens is that sheep, usually growing lambs, grazing stubble or pasture infested with thistles, sustain small injuries on the lower parts of the legs. These become infected with both orf virus and a bacterium called *Dermatophilus congolensis* (this on its own causes mycotic dermatitis, or 'lumpy wool'). The result is bleeding, granulomatous or warty outgrowths from the skin, which may affect a relatively small area at the coronary band, or large areas of the leg below the knee or hock. The diagnosis is usually made on the grounds of the appearance of the lesion on the legs combined with the type of grazing.

Treatment

This is not straightforward because of the combined cause. Since orf is caused by a virus, there is no treatment that will speed up recovery from this. *Dermatophilus*, however, is a bacterium and is sensitive to antibiotics. It is therefore worth asking your vet about the possible use of antibiotic injections. It may also be worth using an antibiotic spray on the lesions, as this may help to reduce secondary infection and speed healing, but recovery is likely to take several weeks and will not happen until the affected animals have mounted their own immune response to the orf virus.

Prevention

As the disease is a sporadic one, it is not possible to prevent it except by improving pasture by reducing the population of thistles. If flocks are infected year after year, it may be worth considering the use

Hygroma on knee – these should generally be left alone unless infected.

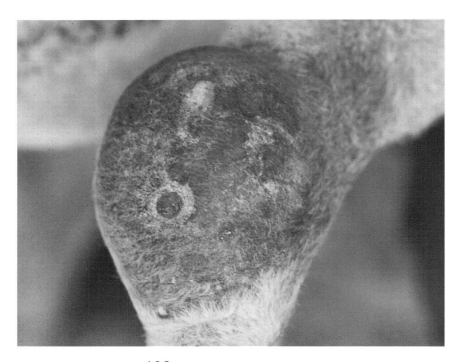

of orf vaccine, but veterinary advice should be sought before doing this.

HYGROMA

This is a swelling over a joint, usually the knee, which is filled with fluid (like 'housemaid's knee' in people). It may be an indication that the animal has been lame in the past and has been spending a lot of time on its knees. Once the swelling is present, it is unlikely to disappear, although the animal may be sound again. It is better not to attempt to do anything with these in the way of treatment, as sticking a needle in or opening them may introduce infection; so leave well alone.

INJECTION-SITE PARALYSIS

There is an important nerve (the tibial nerve) running between the muscles in the back of the thigh, and this is easily damaged if an injection is given at this site, particularly if the technique is not carried out in a sterile manner and infection is introduced, or the injection is rather irritant. When this nerve is damaged the animal stands with a dropped hock and knuckled fetlock, and may have considerable difficulty walking. Some affected animals recover after a time, but others remain with permanent paralysis of the muscles supplied by this nerve. If this is the case, the muscles of the affected leg atrophy and the whole hind leg will be unsuitable for human consumption when the animal is slaughtered.

Prevention

Injections should not be given into the back of the thigh; the neck muscles are the best site, or, if the animal is thin, the quadriceps muscle in the front of the thigh can be used.

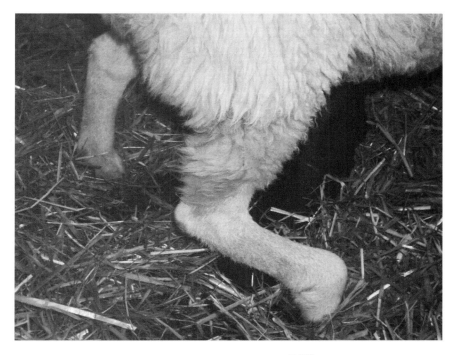

This animal had a partially paralysed leg because of injection-site damage.

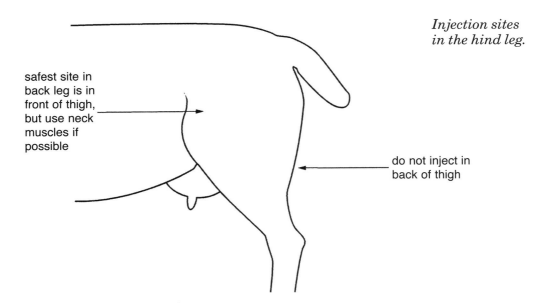

Injection sites in the hind leg.

safest site in back leg is in front of thigh, but use neck muscles if possible

do not inject in back of thigh

OSTEOARTHRITIS

The majority of commercial sheep do not generally live for long enough to develop osteoarthritis, which is generally a disease of sheep of five years of age and older. It can be seen quite commonly in pedigree sheep that are kept for a longer breeding life, and in old pet sheep. The joint most commonly affected is the elbow, and one or both joints may be involved in the individual animal. If only one leg is affected, the sheep is obviously lame and is seen to rest the leg frequently by repeatedly lifting it off the ground. Often it is assumed that the animal has foot lameness, but nothing is found on examination of the lower leg. If both elbows are affected, the sheep walks with a typical restricted gait because it is unable to fully flex both elbows. It spends a lot of time lying down, and when standing, has its front legs tucked under its body in an attempt to ease the discomfort from the enlarged joints. Animals with elbow arthritis do not commonly graze on their knees as do sheep with front foot lameness,

presumably because it is painful to do so. Once you are familiar with the typical appearance, it is easy to recognize. Diagnosis can be confirmed by feeling the size of the elbows and comparing them with those of a normal young sheep. The area around the joint is often two or three times the thickness of a normal elbow because of the amount of new bone that has developed around the joint. It is also not possible to flex the elbow as you can in an unaffected animal. Less commonly, other joints such as the hips may be affected in some old animals.

Treatment

There is no treatment in the long term, as the joint is grossly thickened and distorted with new bone formation. If the animal is a pet, it may be possible to consider with your vet the use of anti-inflammatory drugs, but these cannot generally be used for a prolonged period, so it may be necessary to have the animal put down on humane grounds. With commercial animals that can walk on all feet, it may be legal to transport to a slaughterhouse,

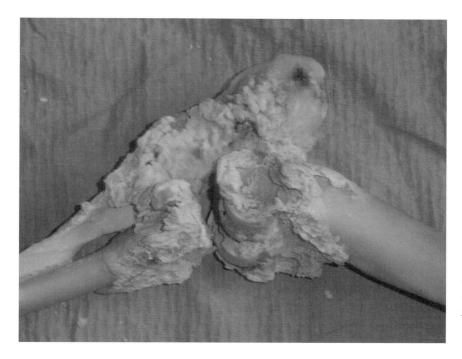

Elbow joint from a ewe with osteoarthritis.

Infected fetlock joint resulting from penetrating injury.

but they should not go into a market. Check with the OVS at the slaughterhouse first. It is interesting to note that ewes with elbow arthritis often improve significantly if they become pregnant, but rapidly revert to their former condition once they have lambed.

Prevention

This is not possible, as it is not known what triggers arthritis to develop in some animals and not in others.

OTHER CAUSES OF ARTHRITIS

Occasional cases of arthritis affecting one or more joints are seen, unrelated to long-term effects of joint ill, erysipelas arthritis or osteoarthritis. These are usually individual cases with no common cause, although infection via an overlying wound is not uncommon. The only disease of flock significance seen in the UK in which some

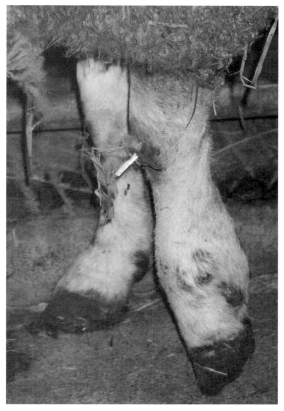

infected animals may present with joint problems is maedi visna (MV). This disease, caused by a slow virus, is better known as a chronic respiratory infection. As well as affecting the lungs (and the nervous system and udder), the virus can also infect joints, producing enlargements; in particular it affects the knees. It is highly unlikely that lameness would be the only sign that this disease was present in a flock, since the respiratory form is much more common. In contrast, in caprine arthritis encephalitis, the related disease in goats, joint involvement rather than respiratory disease is the most common sign, as the name of the disease suggests.

VISNA

This is the neurological form of the viral disease maedi visna, in which damage done by the virus to the brain or spinal cord can cause the animal to have difficulty walking: dragging one back leg is a common presentation. However, as with the arthritic type of this disease, this form is not very likely to be the first and only sign of the presence of the disease in a flock: breathing problems and weight loss are the most common signs.

OSTEOCHONDRITIS DISSECANS (OCD)

This is a degenerative joint disease of rapidly growing animals, particularly males, and is seen in horses, cattle and pigs. There has been at least one reported case affecting the elbow joints in ram lambs being heavily fed for fast growth, so it should be considered by your vet if no other explanation can be found for lameness in this type of animal.

DELAYED SWAYBACK

This is the late onset of a swaying gait affecting the hind limbs caused by copper deficiency; it may occur as late as four months of age, with the animal having been apparently normal up to that stage. Affected animals will not recover, but further deterioration may sometimes be prevented by the administration of copper. However, as copper can be toxic, it should only be given after confirmation of the disease by your veterinary surgeon. For further details, see Chapter 14.

KANGAROO GAIT

This is a rare neurological problem that usually affects lactating ewes, but has also been seen in pregnant ewes. Affected ewes lose the power to use their front legs properly: they either trip over as they walk or, in more advanced cases, are unable to walk with their front legs and move more like a kangaroo – hence the name. If forced to stand, they do so with an arched back, holding all their legs under their body. The condition was first reported in New Zealand, but is also seen sporadically in the UK; in fact I saw four cases in one flock whilst I was writing this chapter. The cause is unknown – there seem to be no disturbances of minerals or vitamins in the animals that have been examined in detail. Investigation has shown damage to the nerves supplying the muscles of the front legs, but in most cases the damage seems to be reversible, with recovery gradually taking place after a few weeks, particularly once the lambs of the affected ewes have been weaned. The best advice currently is to confine affected ewes to a small paddock where they can be given extra feed, or to house and feed adequately, and to wean their lambs as soon as possible.

ACUTE MASTITIS

In the early stages of acute (usually gangrenous) mastitis, affected ewes may drag the back leg, or even be obviously lame, on the same side as the affected half of the udder. It is easy to dismiss this as 'just another lame sheep', so that by the time the real reason becomes apparent it is usually too late to save the affected gland, or in some cases, the life of the ewe herself. It is, therefore, always worth checking the udder if a ewe around peak lactation shows this appearance. If the mastitis is spotted sufficiently early, treatment may be successful in saving the ewe, even if not the half of the udder.

MISCELLANEOUS CONDITIONS ASSOCIATED WITH PREGNANCY AND LAMBING

Heavily pregnant ewes sometimes have difficulty walking for a number of reasons, including pressure on nerves supplying the back legs. Difficulty in lambing, particularly with oversized lambs, may cause damage to the hind-limb nerves, so that the ewe is unable to stand and may lie with the legs stretched out behind her. Keeping her on deep bedding to prevent slipping, combined with the application of a home-made harness to keep the legs under the body, may help to get her back on her feet. Milk fever (hypocalcaemia) will cause ewes, both in late pregnancy and early lactation, to become recumbent. However, an injection of calcium borogluconate under the skin should bring about a rapid response in an uncomplicated case.

16 Minimizing Lameness

This final chapter brings together a summary of the information that has been presented in previous chapters to assist you in achieving and maintaining a healthy flock, with healthy feet, and the minimum of avoidable lameness. I repeat what I said at the beginning of the book that, in spite of all the best endeavours, there will always be some lame sheep. Anyone who has experience of keeping sheep will, I would expect, concur with this view. However, these should largely consist of the unavoidable types of lameness – the accidental injuries, the foot abscesses for which we have no recognized method of prevention, for example, or common problems such as scald that are difficult to prevent but respond well to treatment. All should be treated as soon as is reasonably possible. Lameness has always been one of the major welfare concerns in sheep production. With today's emphasis on high welfare standards, lame sheep will increasingly come under close scrutiny, and it is not acceptable to ignore

Lame animals should be treated as soon as is reasonably possible.

Shepherds should aim for a high standard of welfare whether sheep are outdoors...

...or whether they are housed.

them, for whatever the reason. It is often stated that UK farming has the highest welfare standards in the world. Let's try to make sure that this really is the case.

Here are the main do's and don'ts:

Do take lame sheep seriously

● Recognizing that all lameness cannot be prevented is one thing, doing nothing about it is not acceptable.
● Seek professional help if you are not getting in control of a problem.

Do have the correct equipment appropriate for the size of your flock

● Keep equipment in good, clean, dry condition.
● Have an appropriate handling system so you can get sheep in and examine them with as little physical effort as possible.

Do try to improve overall flock foot health by selection of breeding stock with sound feet

● Pedigree breeders should select for well shaped, healthy feet as well as for production criteria – this is particularly important with rams, which have a major impact on the flock through their offspring.
● Keep records of breeding animals with persistent or repeated foot problems, and give serious consideration to not keeping their offspring.

Do look after your sheep's feet, but don't feel you must trim all of them as a routine

● If a foot is basically sound, leave well alone.
● Try to get any major infectious disease under control – this will mean fewer sheep with misshapen claws, and less work in the long run.

Do examine sufficient affected animals in a flock with a lameness problem to make sure of the correct diagnosis

● There may be more than one condition present – don't assume that all animals are the same as the first one you examine.
● Do be prepared to cull chronically infected animals – these will act as a constant source of infection to others.

Do select the appropriate treatment, based on the diagnosis, and apply it correctly

● Make sure footbaths are made up at the correct strength – measure water and add the appropriate amount of chemical.
● If footrot or CODD are present, you must treat all animals – it is no use just treating obviously lame ones, since there will be many others with a less obvious infection. These untreated ones will carry on infecting others.
● Don't turn newly footbathed sheep immediately back to grass – standing on hard ground for half an hour will allow the chemical a chance to work.
● Consider with your vet giving injectable antibiotics for severe cases of footrot or CODD.

Don't spread infection by gathering groups, including infected animals, into dirty pens and then releasing them without footbathing – this is highly likely to result in increased numbers of infected animals during the following weeks

● If an infectious condition is present in the flock, always footbath after gathering, even if the gather was for a different procedure.
● Try to have handling pens on hard standing that can be cleaned.
● Try to have an area of hard ground where sheep can stand after footbathing.
● Keep pens as clean as possible, and clean out at least at the end of each day.

Don't buy, or bring in footrot or CODD! It is extremely easy to introduce these two important infectious diseases accidentally by taking insufficient care in assessing the health status of animals being added to the flock. This applies whether it is one ram, or large numbers of ewes or store lambs

● Ideally, do not buy groups of animals which contain any lame ones.
● Always keep newly purchased animals, or animals that have been away from the farm, separate for a quarantine period of at least three weeks (for other reasons as well as lameness).
● Examine feet, and footbath during the quarantine period.
● Do not mix with resident sheep until you are quite sure that all their feet are healthy.
● If you suspect you have bought in animals with CODD, consult your vet about the best way to avoid spreading this to the rest of the flock.

Don't cause avoidable foot problems by careless or unskilled trimming

● Overtrimming is the main cause of toe granulomas – don't cause them by cutting too deep.
● There is no need to trim feet unless they are significantly overgrown.
● Trimming should not cause feet to bleed, especially if the feet were basically sound before trimming.

Do make sure that ewes' feet are sound at housing – infectious diseases such as footrot and CODD are likely to spread rapidly during the housing period

● Separate out any lame ewes into one pen so they can be easily treated.

● Footbath before housing, and at intervals during the housing period if practical.
● Recognize that infected feet will contaminate bedding, making infections in young lambs more likely.

Do supply sufficient bedding for housed sheep, especially lambing ewes

● Dirty bedding collects on feet, predisposing to infection with scald.
● Dirty lambing pens are likely to lead to navel ill and joint ill in lambs.

Do make sure that lambs receive sufficient colostrum

● Lack of colostrum predisposes lambs to infections such as joint ill.

Do consult your vet if you have any unexplained lameness, particularly if it affects many animals in the flock, or your normal treatment routine does not seem to be working

● Remember that exotic diseases such as foot and mouth disease could strike again.
● Recognize that new diseases can appear and quickly become established, in the way that, for example, CODD has done.

FINALLY...

I hope this book has helped you to appreciate the wide range of conditions that can lead to lameness in sheep, and that if you have a problem, it will assist you in doing something about it. There is nothing more dispiriting than feeling that you are fighting a losing battle, but nothing more satisfying than winning one: I hope this book gives you the knowledge to do the latter.

Diagrammatic Summary for Diagnosis of Common Foot Lesions

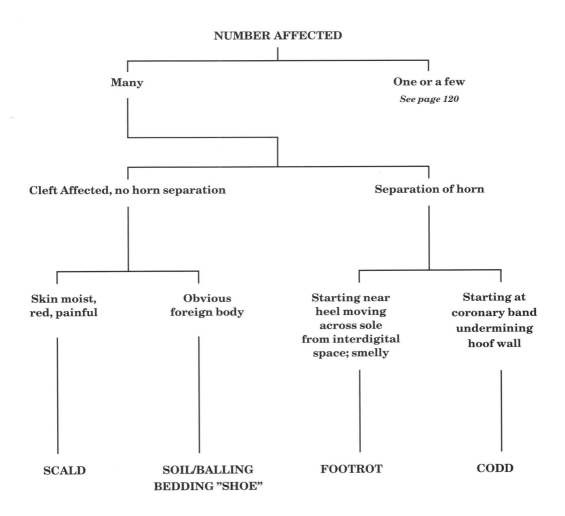

NUMBER AFFECTED

Many   One or a few
See page 120

Cleft Affected, no horn separation   Separation of horn

Skin moist, red, painful   Obvious foreign body   Starting near heel moving across sole from interdigital space; smelly   Starting at coronary band undermining hoof wall

SCALD   SOIL/BALLING BEDDING "SHOE"   FOOTROT   CODD

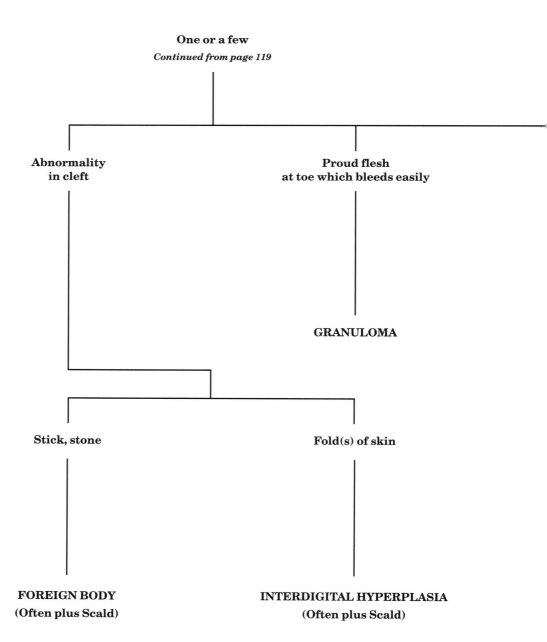

One or a few
Continued from page 119

**Abnormality
in cleft**

**Proud flesh
at toe which bleeds easily**

GRANULOMA

Stick, stone

Fold(s) of skin

FOREIGN BODY
(Often plus Scald)

INTERDIGITAL HYPERPLASIA
(Often plus Scald)

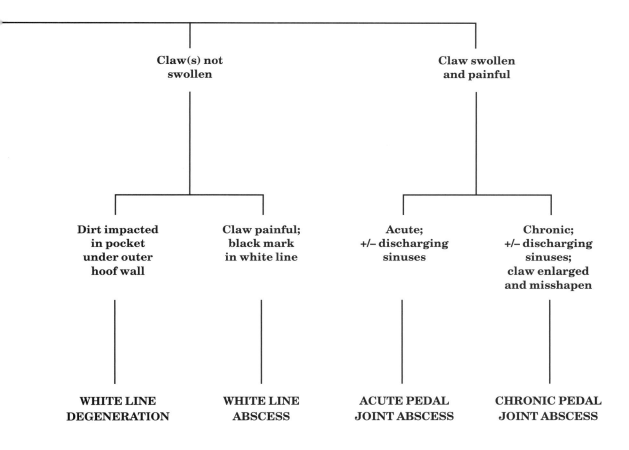

Diagrammatic Summary for Eradication of Footrot

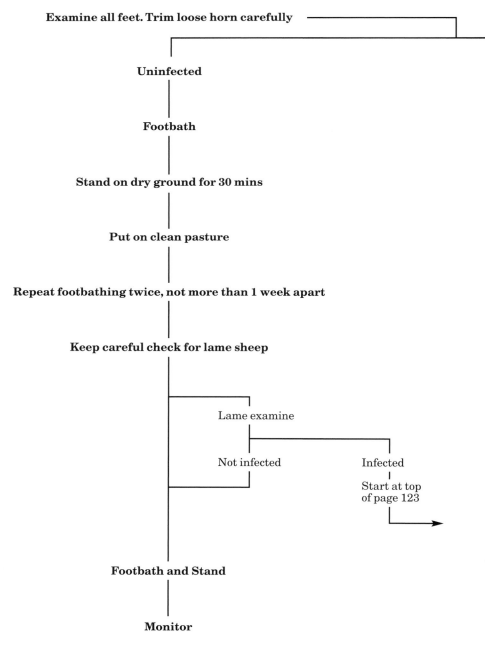

Examine all feet. Trim loose horn carefully

Uninfected

Footbath

Stand on dry ground for 30 mins

Put on clean pasture

Repeat footbathing twice, not more than 1 week apart

Keep careful check for lame sheep

Lame examine

Not infected   Infected

Start at top
of page 123

Footbath and Stand

Monitor

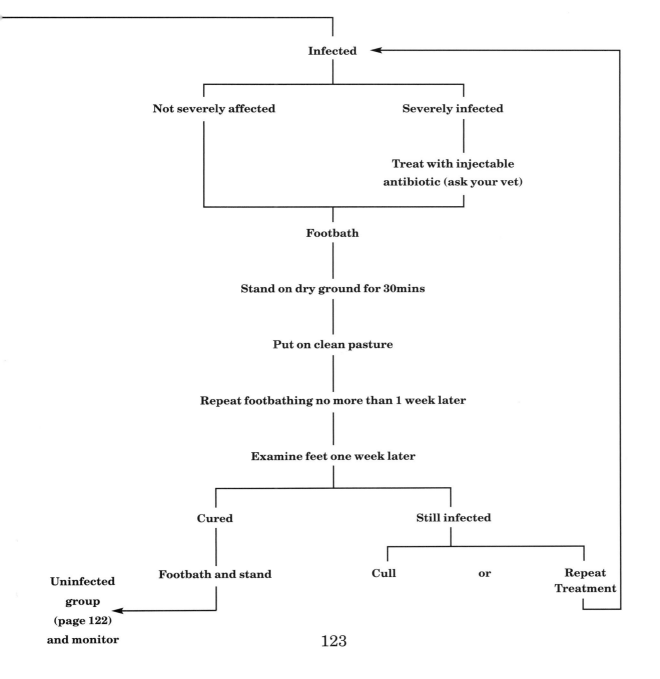

Infected

Not severely affected   Severely infected

Treat with injectable
antibiotic (ask your vet)

Footbath

Stand on dry ground for 30mins

Put on clean pasture

Repeat footbathing no more than 1 week later

Examine feet one week later

Cured   Still infected

Footbath and stand   Cull   or   Repeat
                                                    Treatment

Uninfected
group
(page 122)
and monitor

123

Glossary

Abaxial – furthest away from midline, for example of a digit or other body part

Acidosis – increase in acidity of rumen usually caused by eating excess of carbohydrates

Acute – sudden onset of condition or illness

Adjuvant – substance added to vaccine to increase immune response by animal

Anaerobic – living in absence of oxygen

Ankylose/ankylosis – adjacent bones becoming fused together as result of disease in joint separating them

Antibody – protective substance produced by certain specialised cells in body which protect against specific disease-causing organisms

Atrophy – reduction in size e.g. of muscle through lack of use or loss of nerve supply

Axial – nearest the midline e.g. of a digit or other body part

Benign – mild or non-invasive

Biotin – a vitamin of B group, also called vitamin H

Chronic – prolonged condition or illness

CODD – contagious ovine digital dermatitis

Corium – layer of skin or hoof that contains many blood vessels and nerves

Coronary band – junction of horny hoof and normal skin

DEFRA – Department for Environment and Rural Affairs

Dermatitis – inflammation of skin

Dermis – deepest layer of the skin

Dichelobacter nodosus – the latin name for the bacteria that cause footrot

Digit – most distant parts of leg, equivalent to human fingers and toes

Disarticulate/disarticulation – separate bones by cutting through the joint between them

Distal – furthest away from a point of reference, e.g. most distant point of body part

Epidermis – outer layer of skin

Enzyme – substance that helps a chemical reaction take place without itself being changed

Fibroma – a non-malignant lump of fibrous tissue

FMD – Foot and Mouth Disease

Fusobacterium necrophorum – the latin name for the bacteria that cause scald

Granulation tissue – very vascular tissue that is produced during healing of a wound

Granuloma – excessive production of granulation tissue

Hyperplasia – increased production of normal tissue

Hygroma – swelling over joint filled with fluid produced as result of repeated injury

Interdigital – area between the hooves or claws

Intramuscular – into a muscle, e.g. an injection

Keratin – very hard substance from which horn is made
Keratinized – tissue that has become filled with keratin

Laminae – microscopic thin flat structures like the leaves of a book
Laminitis – inflammation of the laminae
Lateral – part or side of body furthest from midline
Lesion – area of tissue damaged by disease or injury

Malignant – disease that becomes progressively worse
Medial – part or side of body nearest to midline
Metabolic/metabolism – relating to the chemical reactions that take part in the body, mostly to do with use of end products of digestion
Metritis – inflammation of the uterus (womb)
Moxidectin – chemical name for a particular wormer
MV – shorthand for maedi visna, a slowly-developing disease caused by a virus
Myopathy – a disorder of muscle

Osteoarthritis – degenerative, usually painful, changes in joints that occur as an animal gets older
OVS – Official Veterinary Surgeon working in an abattoir

Papillae – microscopic or very small protuberances
Periople – area of soft horn at top of hoof linking hard horn with normal skin above
Phalanx – one of bones of digit
Polyarthritis – inflammation or infection of more than one joint
Prevalence – number of cases of a disease or condition within a group at a specific time
Protease – an enzyme that attacks and breaks down protein substances
Proximal – nearest to a point of reference, e.g. nearest point to a body part

Quadriceps – the large muscle in the upper hindleg, lying in front of the thigh bone

SARA – sub-acute ruminal acidosis
Sebaceous – gland in skin producing waxy secretion
Serogroup – category or sub-group into which e.g. bacteria are placed based on laboratory tests using antibodies
Subcutaneous – under the skin e.g. injection
Surfactant – detergent added to a liquid that increases its wetting properties
Systemic illness – affecting the whole body with obvious signs of illness

Vesicle – fluid-filled blister in skin
Virulent – severe form of disease

White line – area which lies at junction of wall and sole horn in a hoof, so called because it is white in colour

Index

Abscess, lamb's claw 100–1
  lamb's foot 100–1
  pedal joint 45–6, 76–80
  spinal 104
  toe 43–4
  white line 43–4, 69–70
Aerosol sprays 33–4
Anatomy, foot 12–18
  variation in 12–13
Antibiotic footbath 32, 58
  disposal of 33
Antibiotics 28, 32
  injectable 34–5, 58–9, 74, 101
Antibiotic spray 33–4, 49, 58
Arcanobacterium pyogenes 97
Arthritis, erysipelas 105–6
  infectious 96–9
  other types 111–2
  osteo– 110–11
  poly– 96–9

Bath, foot (*see* footbath)
Bleeding, causing 22, 24, 26, 56, 73, 74

Claw, anatomy of 14–18
  corkscrew 26
  deformity 21, 26
  swelling of 38, 45, 78
CODD 42–3, 64–8
  control and prevention 67–8
  diagnosis 64–7
  treatment 67
Conformation 21
Contagious ovine digital dermatitis
    (*see* CODD)
Copper sulphate 32, 33, 84

Corium 17–20, 83
Corkscrew claw 26
Coronary band 14, 38, 45, 64, 70, 76
Costs, of lameness 8
Cracks in hoof 24, 38–9, 44–5, 74, 88– 90,
  91–2
Crates, turn-over 10–11
Culling 61–2

Deformities, limb 95
Dermatophilus congolensis 108
Diagnosis, overview 37–47, 119–21
Dichelobacter nodosus 35, 52
Dip baths 107
Disposal, footbath solutions 33

Economics 8
Elbow joint 110–11
Embryo death 7
Erysipelas 97, 105–6
  prevention 106
  treatment 106
  vaccine 106–7
Erysipelothrix rhusiopathiae 97, 105, 107
Escherichia coli 97

Feet, examination of 23, 37–9
    misshapen 26, 55, 61
  trimming 22–7, 56
Fertilizer burn 87
Fibroma 40–1, 87
Footbaths 11, 28–30
Footbathing 28–32, 49–51, 56–8, 59–61,
Foot, anatomy of 12–18
  knives 10
  shears 10

Footrot 41, 52–63
  benign 52, 53, 56
  chronic 61–2
  control 60–2
  diagnosis 53–6
  eradication 62–3, 122–3
  resistance to 63
  strawberry 108–9
  treatment 56–60
  transmission periods 53
  vaccine 58–9
  virulent 41–2, 52, 53–5, 56
Foreign body 39, 90, 96
Formalin 31, 58
  disposal 33
Fractures 94, 105
Fusobacterium necrophorum 48, 52, 97

Granulation tissue 45–6, 77, 81
Granuloma 22, 46, 81–4
  cause 81–3
  diagnosis 83–4
  prevention 84
  treatment 84
Grooves, horn 20, 38–9, 46, 88

Handling systems 10, 29
Hock joint 21
Hoof, structure of 15–18
Horn capsule 15–17
  detachment of 38, 43, 55, 67
Horn, formation of 18–20
  grooves in 20, 38–9, 46, 88
  growth rate 19
  overgrowth 12, 24–5, 56
Hygroma 109
Hyperplasia, interdigital 40–1, 87

Injectable antibiotics 34–5, 58–9, 74, 101
Injection sites 35, 109–10
Injection site paralysis 109–10
Injection technique 35, 109
Interdigital cleft, impaction of 39–40
  infection of 40, 48–9
Interdigital gland 14–15, 87–8
Interdigital hyperplasia 40–1, 87

Joint ill 96–9

diagnosis 97
prevention 97
treatment 97–9

Kangaroo gait 112
Keratin 19
Knives, foot 10

Lambing–associated lameness 113
Lambs, lameness in 93–104
Laminae 17, 19, 43, 88
Laminitis 46, 88–90
  diagnosis 88
  prevention 90
  treatment 90
Ligaments 18
Limbs, conformation 21
Lime 36

Maedi visna 112
Maggots, in feet 23, 52, 55
Manure balling 85–6
Mastitis 113
Mats, absorbent 28, 30
Milking sheep 28
Misshapen feet 26, 55, 61
Molybdenum 103
Moxidectin 36
Myopathy, nutritional 101–3

Navicular bone 18
Nutritional myopathy 101–3

Orf virus 108
Osteoarthritis 110–11
Osteochronditis dissecans 112
Overparing, feet 22, 24, 73, 81–2
Oxytetracycline, injection 34, 100
  spray 33, 49

Papillae, 17–18
Paring, feet 22–7, 56
Pasterns, sloping 21
Pedal bone 18
Pedal joint 18
Pedal joint abscess 45–6, 76–80
  diagnosis 78
  treatment 78–80

Penicillin 106
Penicillin/streptomycin 34
Periople 16
Phalanx, third (*see* pedal bone)
Pigmentation, horn 17
    wool 36
Polyarthritis, infectious 96–9
    neonatal 96–9
Post–dipping lameness 107–8
Pregnant sheep, treating 59
Prevalence, lameness 6
Proud flesh (*see* granuloma)
Pus, in foot 18, 43–4, 45, 70, 73, 78, 96, 100
Pus, in joints 96–101
Pyaemia, tick 99
Pyrethroid, synthetic 100

'Quick' (*see* corium)

Redfoot 101
Rickets 103

Scald 30, 38, 40, 48–51
    control 51, 63
    diagnosis 40, 48–9
    treatment 49–51, 63
Selenium 101–3
Shears, foot 10, 24
Shelly hoof 43, 69
Sinuses, discharging 38, 45, 78
Soil balling 39–40, 85–6
Sole, structure 20
Spinal abscess 104
Splints 94–5
Spray, antibiotic 33–4, 49, 58
Staphylococcus aureus 99
Stiff lamb disease 101–3
Strawberry footrot 108–9

Streptococcus dysgalactiae 96
Strike, fly 23, 52, 55
Surfactant 32
Swayback 103–4
    delayed 103, 112
Synthetic pyrethroid 100

Tendon sheaths 18
Tendons 18
Thorns, in feet 96, 105
Tick-borne fever 99
Tick pyaemia 99
Tilmycosin 34–5, 62
Trimming, feet 22–7, 56
    technique 24–7
    unskilled 22
Tubules, horn 19, 20
Turn-over crates 10–11

Vaccination, erysipelas 107–8
    footrot 35–6, 58–9
Visna 112
Vitamin E 101–3

Welfare Code 6
White line 16–17, 20, 69
    abscess 43–4
    degeneration 43, 69
    separation 25, 43, 69
White line lesions 43–4, 69–75
    cause 70–3
    diagnosis 73
    prevention 75
    treatment 73–5
White muscle disease 101–3

Zinc sulphate 31–2, 51, 56–8, 59–61, 62
    disposal 33